Dedicated to
my great grandfather
George Wood,
bone-setter

A ZEN APPROACH TO
BODYTHERAPY

A ZEN APPROACH TO
BODYTHERAPY

From Rolf to Feldenkrais to Tanouye Roshi

WILLIAM S. LEIGH

The Institute of Zen Studies

Honolulu, Hawaii

1987

Copyright © 1987 by The Institute of Zen Studies

ISBN 0-8248-1099-6

Library of Congress Cataloging-in-Publication Data
Leigh, William S., 1914–
  A Zen approach to bodytherapy.

  Bibliography: p.
  1. Mind and body therapies. 2. Zen Buddhism—
Psychology. I. Title. II. Title: Zen approach to
body therapy.
RC489.M53h45   1987   615.5   86-82995
ISBN 0-2849-1099-6 (pbk.)

CONTENTS

FOREWORD

As a therapist working with the humanistic psychotherapies, it is easy to accept the notion that the mind and musculoskeletal system each express in their own way our total human experience. For me this is a fact, a useful and powerful one. Despite this, it is an idea which has not yet gained acceptance by the mainstream of our health care providers. This is perhaps attributable to the mind-body separation that is still part of our culture's belief-system. Since we have in our language two separate words which create a distinction between these functions, mind and body, we are drawn to a spurious duality concerning their relationship to each other. No dictionary which I consulted, including medical ones, contained a definition of the word "bodytherapy," by which I mean manipulation of the body to effect changes in it and consequently in our awareness of self. Other possible alternatives such as "body psychotherapy" or "somatic psychology" are also not to be found. The word "psychophysical" is applied more to psychophysics.

In modern times, it was Wilhelm Reich (a member of Freud's circle) who first described character armor, the literal rigidification and distortion of the musculature expressing mental and emotional dysfunction. He went on to identify various body points to manipulate in order to treat the distress. Other distinguished names which followed his lead include Lowen who developed Bioenergetics, Rolf with Structural Integration (Rolfing) and Feldenkrais with Functional Integration. These techniques reflect a similar philosophy, that what we hold in our bodies, we also hold in our minds. From this it follows that affecting one affects the other and that each springs from a monistic source of our life's experience. Bodytherapy, through awareness of the physical expression of mental and emotional events, is also a *psychotherapy*. Paraphrasing Fritz Perls, awareness alone may be curative.

We may now have some cause for optimism that belief in the duality of mind and body will wither and die. There is recent and clear evidence from the medical sciences showing a direct relation between mood and the functioning of our endocrinologic and immunologic systems, the connection between thinking and the somatic symptoms of anxiety we have all experienced. In Dub Leigh's present book, we also have ample phenomenologic evidence of the mind-body continuum and how intervention along the continuum is reciprocal throughout.

Bodytherapy is for me a very moving record of one man's pilgrimage seeking the highest attainment in the practice of bodytherapy and in the personal growth available to him and his clients through that practice. Dub Leigh is indeed special in his experience of, and certification in, three powerful bodytherapy disciplines, those of Ida Rolf, Moshe Feldenkrais, and Tanouye Tenshin Roshi. He must be the only person ever with these credentials. We are privileged to have an account of his experiences with the masters, as well as of his own mastery and integration of their therapies. We are even more in his debt for sharing his own unique history.

Dub is now integrating into his bodytherapy what other therapists have been integrating into their verbal therapies. It is remarkable to me how his study of Zen Bodytherapy is equally a reflection of the growth of transpersonal themes in Western psychology as it absorbs some of the teachings of the Eastern liberation religions. For those who seek the path of ego transcendence, it will come as no surprise that bodytherapy may also be a guide.

Oh, one more thing. I have personally experienced Dub's genius at bodytherapy. Believe me, he does good work.

ED HERSHGOLD, M.D.

University of Utah, School of Medicine
May 1986

PREFACE

THERE WAS a point in my life when I was just about leveled by despair. I was successful in business and community affairs, but there was no inner purpose. I had overshot my goals. I hated my work, my life, my self. My despair hurt so much that I was forced to get into something new. This something new was the deep desire to be of service. This desire turned my life around. It changed my career, my location, my lifestyle, my philosophy, everything.

I saw a lot of suffering in people's bodies. I knew that if the body is aberrated, so are the feelings and thoughts. I wanted to assist, and because of my physique and nature, I knew that body work was the way I could assist best. I have always been a hands-on kind of person. I express my feelings through touch rather than words.

I've been fortunate the second half of my life. I've done what I wanted to do. I am one of two people in the world to have been personally trained and certified by both Ida Rolf and Moshe Feldenkrais, two of the most brilliant body scientists and therapists in the Western world. Then after twenty years of work in the field, I met Tanouye Tenshin Roshi, a master of Zen and the healing and martial arts of Japan. Under his guidance I am developing a method of bodytherapy integrating what I've learned about structure and function with the Eastern teachings of the circulation of vital energy.

I wrote this book to share my experiences and to introduce you to the wonderful teachers who taught me so much about the wisdom of the body. Actually it would be easier for me to tell my story with my hands. I'd just say, "Climb up on the table and I'll show you what I know, right on your own body." I can't do that, of course. But if I can't touch you in one way, maybe I can in another.

ACKNOWLEDGEMENTS

I WOULD LIKE to acknowledge my teachers, Ida P. Rolf, Ph.D., Moshe Feldenkrais, Sc.D., and Tanouye Tenshin Roshi. Without their friendship, this book would not have been written.

I also want to thank the following: Jack Swartz, Alethia Foundation, who planted the seed for this book by predicting ten years ago that I would write; Betty Fuller who started me writing; Edith Lozier who constantly supported me; Audrey Nakumura who gave the final loving push to get the job done; two psychiatrists, Edward Hershgold, M.D., and David Berenson, M.D., who acted as consultants; Carol Costello and Naomi Steinfeld, who edited and outlined; another consultant, Allan Rudolf, Ph.D., the only other person in the world trained and certified personally by both Ida Rolf and Moshe Feldenkrais; Neal Powers, president of the Rolf Institute, for his guidance and assistance; Alon Talmi, Moshe's first student, for correcting Moshe's biography; Doris Levy and Gordon Greene for many hours of talented proofreading and editing; and especially Mike Sayama, Ph.D., a master editor who really tied my manuscript into a book.

I am also grateful for the beautiful and nurturing homes I found at the Esalen Institute and Chozen-ji/International Zen Dojo, during my years of searching.

A ZEN APPROACH TO
BODYTHERAPY

MY TRANSFORMATION

IN SOUTHERN UTAH, they say I come from good, old Mormon pioneer stock. My grandmother was the first white baby to be born in Iron County. My great grandfather William Berry was shot and killed by a mob because he practiced polygamy as a Mormon. My father was a successful merchant and the town mayor. My mother was a school teacher.

I was the family black sheep. At twelve I slipped from the Mormon fold and refused to go to church. I was as wild as a March hare during my junior high, high school, and college years. Getting drunk, wrecking cars, shooting up hotels, and fighting with the police, eventually I was kicked in and out of colleges from Chicago to Oregon. My father sent me a monthly check to stay out of the state. He finally disowned me when I came back to Utah and got into a mess. That was the best thing he did for me. I cleaned up the mess without help.

In 1934 after years of being in and out of college, I began learning the furniture business: the manufacturing end at the largest West Coast factory, Dorenbacker Manufacturing of Portland, Oregon, and the distribution end from the Los Angeles branch of William Volker, the world's largest distributor of furniture and floor coverings.

World War II interrupted my business education. Pearl Harbor was on Sunday, and Monday morning I went down to the post office to join the Navy. The line was half a block long. So I walked over to the Marine Corps recruiting office where there was no line, only a sergeant and an officer. I told them I had tried enlisting in the Army the year before but had been turned down for a physical condition. I asked if they would take me. The sergeant asked me if I was breathing. I said, "Yes," and he said I was in.

From 1941 until 1945 I served two tours of combat duty in the South Pacific as a non-commissioned officer trained in communications. I was proud of my record as a master sergeant. Under combat stress my mind and body seemed to function better for longer periods of time than those of almost anyone I had an opportunity to compare myself with. I used to say that I could walk further on my guts than most people could on their legs.

After the war I returned to Utah as a hero in my family's eyes and went into the retail furniture business. For twenty years, seven days a week, twelve to eighteen hours a day, I plugged away. I married, raised two children, and ended up owning three furniture stores, a small finance company, and a small real estate company. I attended every type of business and marketing seminar given from New York to Chicago to Carmel. I studied salesmanship and human motivation and trained dozens of sales people. Many are operating successful businesses today.

For example, I picked up a nineteen-year-old who could not hold a job. He was in trouble with his pregnant wife, his own family, his in-laws, and the law. The only thing going for him was that he came from a highly-respected family. I agreed to hire him and train him, I guaranteed that at the end of one year he would be making ten times more than he had ever made. In return I asked that he agree to do whatever I asked and to do so without question or grumbling. He agreed! Six days a week from 7:30 in the morning till late at night, we trained. In nine months he was the top salesman in three stores and the recipient of the Junior Chamber of Commerce award as the outstanding young man of the year in our community. He also bought a home, had a son, and was the pride and joy of his family and in-laws.

I was very active in community youth affairs and served as county youth committee chairman and board member for twelve years. Our greatest success was setting up an employment program for problem youngsters. We set up the machinery whereby government and corporations furnished supervisors and paid youngsters to do productive work. They performed some jobs better than adults could in the mountains and deserts. I also worked

2

closely with the local probation officers, and many problem youngsters were placed with me as an employer/teacher.

During this twenty year period, I was president, officer, or commander of almost every civic organization: the Rotary Club, Chamber of Commerce, P.T.A., American Indian Council, Boy Scouts, the American Legion, and the Veterans of Foreign Wars. For many years I was chairman of the county Democratic committee and a member of the State Central Committee of the Democratic Party. I also taught in the Mormon church and was ordained to the priesthood as an Elder.

Despite all of this I was not fulfilled and was drowning in alcohol. I had started drinking at the age of twelve. As a young man I drank recklessly. Once I woke up in a strange flop hotel with a bunch of empty bottles and three dollars. I did not know what day it was or where I was. The last I could remember I was in Salt Lake City. I got a paper and found I was in Chicago. Almost a week that I could not account for had passed.

As the years went on, I learned to plan my drinking. I would free up the time, buy the booze, and then hole up in a hotel room. I would lie on the bed numb for days. As soon as I could rub my forehead and feel my fingers, it was time for another drink. During my last drinking years, I preferred to drink alone and never drank unless I had a few days to get drunk.

The last drunk I planned did not materialize. I planned it while walking back from the hospital. My first son had just died a few days after the doctor had pulled him to pieces getting him out. I told my wife of our loss, and we cried for awhile. Then I kissed her, left my car in the hospital lot, and walked the many blocks to our apartment. Each step took me deeper into apathy.

As I walked on, I remembered my half-hearted suicide attempt when I was a kid. I remembered how I woke up in the hospital with a painful throbbing in my right wrist. I lay there ashamed and disgusted with myself for not doing the job right. I finally got out of bed and searched the room for anything sharp to cut the stitches. But there was nothing. So with the fingernails of my left hand, I dug the stitches out and got the blood flowing again.

The nurse came, then the doctor. They re-sewed the stitches and put me in a straitjacket. As I lay there, I heard the whine of a buzz saw ripping through logs, a sound I had heard often at the Utah sawmills. I clenched my eyes shut. As the blade tore through the log, its scream came closer and closer; then it would get quiet again as the blade drew back to start on another log. I opened my eyes and saw that each time the blade dipped out of the ceiling it came closer and closer. To no avail I struggled to break free of the straitjacket. My terror built with each stroke. Finally I had to exhale and push back into the bed to keep my chest from being ripped apart. God, what a relief when the blade did not touch me. But then it came again, and I knew this time it would get me. The screaming blade came on and on. I cried out and lunged into it. Then it was over. I was on the floor, weeping. All this was a long time ago.

When I reached our apartment, it was six P.M., and the liquor store did not close until eight. I had twenty-eight dollars, enough for a few fifths. I threw myself on the bed. There was no person, no God I could turn to for comfort. Just me. I began sobbing and beating the bed. After a while I stopped and looked out the window a few minutes. Then slowly I turned my eyes back into the room and said aloud, "There is no place to go but inside."

I struck my midsection with my fist. Something inside my body broke loose and spread as if in the blood stream, carrying a warm glow from my solar plexus in all directions. A complete serenity was carried from cell to cell into every fiber of my body. By the time the warmth reached my toes, I was sleeping peacefully.

I awoke at three in the morning, undressed, went back to sleep, and got up refreshed the next day. Only sometime later did I realize that my compulsion to drink was gone and has remained gone for over thirty years.

I went back to Leigh Furniture Company and county affairs. One day a friend called to kid me about being the biggest individual taxpayer in Iron County. I angrily denied it, but eventually I realized what he said was true. I was more successful than I had ever expected, and I was still not happy. I became very despondent. My depression got worse when Karl, a loved and trusted employee, slowly died of emphysema, and another died in a car accident on company business.

My wife finally got me to the family doctor who sent me to the medical school of the University of Utah. They said I had overshot my goals and advised me to get into a field where I could assist people to make their lives better. But I had lost interest in living and began finding it hard to breathe. The doctors said I had emphysema. Again I just wanted to die and get it over with.

Around this time in the mid-sixties I was asked to represent Iron County in a month-long workshop held by National Training Laboratories at the College of Southern Utah. The purpose was to bring trouble-making Black leaders, student activists, and the leaders of the establishment together to live and work to see if we changed both as individuals and as a group. I had nothing to lose, so I packed my bags and walked the few hundred feet from my home to the campus.

As I entered the meeting place, I saw a big Black guy sitting cross-legged. I introduced myself as representing the local Rotary Club and the county and gave the Chamber of Commerce welcoming speech. He refused my hand and said, "Go fuck off!" A month later, this same man waited for me to take him to the airport for his flight back to Chicago. There were tears in our eyes when we hugged each other good bye.

The NTL participants were divided into groups of three. Mine consisted of Billie, a young Black girl from Minnesota who was trained in social work, a sixty-year old Jewish hospital administrator from Chicago, myself, and an NTL facilitator. We were given four hours to complete a task.

I had one hell of a time getting the job done. The little Black girl kept trying to interrupt and confuse things. But I humored her and pushed the project through. The administrator did the paperwork. The NTL facilitator just sat there and took notes.

After the session, as the facilitator and I were walking down the hall, I commented that we got the job done in spite of the Black girl. The facilitator replied, "Do you know how many times you interrupted Billie? Twenty-nine." I protested that we would not have accomplished anything if I had not shut her up.

At three in the morning I was awake and restless. I could not forget my chat with the facilitator and his look. I kept thinking about shutting Billie off twenty-nine times, and I remembered her saying time after time, "Dub, you're not hearing me." Now I knew it was true. I had thought that she was Black, female, young and stupid, and had to be squashed if we were going to get the job done. I got the roster of participants out and found that Billie held down a big, responsible job in Minnesota. It didn't make sense that she could be stupid and nonproductive. I walked the campus eating crow the rest of the night.

When Billie came out at six-thirty the next morning, I was waiting on the steps of her dormitory to tell her exactly what I'd realized. We embraced and cried. We were still holding each other and crying as we walked into the cafeteria for breakfast. Five of my cousins were serving food, and they watched their white, married, Mormon cousin come into breakfast crying with his arm around a young Black girl. The turmoil in food preparing and serving was unbelievable that morning.

The day before our NTL group broke up, I sat facing the wall, thinking of the world I had to go back to. I turned to a facilitator and said, "I don't want to go back."

She answered simply, "Then why go back?"

The question hit me like a sledgehammer. I had never even allowed myself to think of separating from Leigh Furniture Company. All kinds of feelings bubbled up inside of me. Tears streamed down my face. I said, "I'm not going back." Then I turned and faced the wall for a long time.

A few days later a Harvard professor who had been in our NTL group called me from the Esalen Institute in Big Sur, California. He suggested that the Esalen programs were just what I needed to find a new life with the goal of serving. I went down there for a month. After I returned home, I got a call from the director, John Heider. He asked me if I was interested in going to Esalen as a resident. He said he had nine hundred and twelve applications out of which twelve would be chosen and asked if I wanted to be one of them. I said, "Yes." The next morning I left Utah, my business, and my family for a new life.[1]

STRUCTURAL INTEGRATION

GETTING ROLFED

PART OF MY residency training at Esalen was to receive ten sessions of Rolfing, a method of bodywork designed by Ida Rolf to balance both sides of the body with each other and to align the major segments of the body, the head, shoulders, thorax, pelvis, and legs, with the gravitational field of the Earth. The Rolfer accomplishes this by freeing the connective tissue of the body from aberrations which have accumulated from either physical or psychological trauma.

My First Session

The first session works over large portions of the body to release aberrations from the body's superficial tissue. The chest is worked to free the rib cage, to improve breathing, and to provide more oxygen for the body. The hips, the hip joints, and upper legs are worked to free the legs from the pelvis. The area around the twelfth rib, the crest of the ilium, the neck, and the back are also worked on.

I had heard a lot of people complain of the pain, but I did not doubt that I could go through it without much problem after all I had gone through in the war. However, I was not prepared for the pain that surfaced. Wherever the Rolfer put his fingers, knuckles, or elbows, old pains I had buried came up to be experienced and released. But it was a different kind of pain, often accompanied by burning, and when the pressure stopped, the pain was replaced by a good feeling. Sometime the good feeling was there with the pain.

Then there was the poison. I could taste it in my mouth and smell it on my breath. The Rolfer said my poisons were coming out of their hiding places and going into my body fluids and being released into the air.

My Second Session

The second session is a continuation of the first, with work on the knees, ankles, feet, shoulders, and back. The legs are brought into better alignment with the pelvis to give the individual better grounding with the earth.

The day before my second session I guess I thought I could float when I came out of a seminar. I ran along the top of a stone wall and jumped, expecting to land on soft green grass eight feet below. There was plenty of grass, but I snapped two of my toes on a rock. I told my Rolfer, but he said we just would not pay attention to them.

The Rolfer started with the good foot first, and all the old trauma buried there came out. My foot was an 8½ F width. Until the war, I did not even know shoes came that wide so I went through my early years jamming my feet into shoes that were much too narrow. Then came the Marines and forced marches with full equipment. The pain in my misshapen feet became so strong that I shut it off. Even when blood sloshed in my boots, I felt nothing. It was as if my feet were frozen; it was my survival.

When the Rolfer started working my good foot, it began to tingle as life and feeling came back, something like recovering from frost bite. Then the real pain started. I experienced past times and places when I had buried my face and silently cried.

The Rolfer gave me some time to compose myself before starting on the foot with the two broken toes. To my surprise even with the two broken toes, this foot was not as painful and did not take as long. Then he worked the shoulders. This was a breeze, really a joy after the feet. I left the ordeal feeling good about my Rolfer and myself.

My Third Session

The third session concentrates on lengthening the sides to make breathing more efficient and the trunk more mobile. The body is balanced and lengthened by the end of the third session.

This session was easy. There was some pain in the ribs and some old coughing and choking, but after the second session, the third was a pleasure.

My Fourth and Fifth Session

The fourth session works on the pelvic muscles that connect into the legs and the trunk. The fifth works on the pelvic muscles that connect above the pelvis. These two sessions are usually completed in the same week.

After working on the inside of my legs and into my belly for over an hour and a half, the Rolfer said that we had better call it quits. I would see him Monday morning which was just two days off for the fifth session. It had been a tough session for both of us. The Rolfer weighed about one hundred seventy five, and I was well over two hundred. When it came time for him to get through my belly to work the psoas muscle down near the back bone, he just did not seem to have the strength and weight. He kept trying and trying, but his hands would just not go down that far.

The next day a friend and I drove from Esalen to the Esalen Experimental Ward at the Agnew Hospital in San Jose. After finishing our work there, we went to stay overnight with some friends in Palo Alto. When we got there I told my friend and hosts that I felt very uneasy, unsettled, and ungrounded. I excused myself from dinner saying that I felt a need to be alone and walk. It was six at night when I started my walk, and at three in the morning I was still walking. I came to a motel and thought that maybe after a hot bath I could sleep. I rented a room, took a bath, and lay on the bed. Sleep would not come; I just tossed and turned. Finally I gave up and walked the many miles back to my friend's house, arriving around nine.

My friends suggested I call my Rolfer. He said the effects were definitely due to the Rolfing and explained that the lower half of my pelvis had been worked but the upper half had not been. He said he would balance my body as soon as I could get back to Esalen. I caught a plane to Monterey and got back as soon as I could. What a relief it was to have the Rolfer start the fifth session! The uneasiness was replaced by tranquility and a feeling of being solidly grounded. All seemed to be well with the world.

11

Later I often heard Ida say that the fourth and fifth sessions were actually one big, long session. She insisted that the time between the fourth and fifth be just long enough to allow the body to recuperate from the work of the fourth before doing the fifth.

My Sixth Session

The sixth session works the back of the legs, buttocks, and the back. It continues to open and lengthen the entire body. After this session, the structure of the legs and trunk is mobile and fairly balanced, but the neck is usually still too far forward.

This session was uneventful. There was almost no pain. The Rolfer kept complaining that my buttocks were too small. He said his job was to fluff up my buns.

My Seventh Session

The seventh session worked the neck and head muscles, positioning the head over the center of the shoulders. Some work is done inside the mouth.

I grabbed the Rolfer's hands when he tried to clean off my clavicle. For years I had been "ticklish" when anyone put their hands near the base of my neck. But I finally told the Rolfer to go ahead. Soon I was lost in the pain and ticklishness. A picture of my old family home in Utah came up. It was autumn. There were leaves from the apple tree on the grass. A faucet was dripping. I saw some kids in a circle. There were my brother, my cousin, and two neighbor kids. Then I saw three kids struggling on the ground. Two were trying to hold the third one down, and he was fighting furiously to get up. One kid had an arm around his neck.

I yelled, "They're choking that kid. My God, it's me!" As I said this, I grabbed the Rolfer by the head and threw him across the room. Then I screamed, beat the table, and finally went away. It must have looked like I had passed out.

After a long time, I heard this voice echoing down a tunnel. I finally made out the words, "Can you hear me? Dub, can you hear me?"

I opened my eyes and said, "Yes." The Rolfer then asked me to look where his hands were. They were right on the base of my neck under the clavicles. The ticklishness and the pain were gone and are still gone.

The Rolfer had had enough, so he put me together a little and let me go. I walked from the Esalen baths to Fritz Perls' house where I was assisting in a Gestalt workshop. A little psychiatrist from New York asked me what had happened at the Rolfing session. I told him I did not want to talk about it. He answered that it was unfair to the group if I did not share. I walked over, picked up the little fellow, and carrying him over my head, I walked toward the porch overhanging the cliff. The startled group grabbed the two of us when they saw I was serious. The scared psychiatrist hurried to the office, checked out, and went back to the safety of New York.

At daybreak the day after my seventh session, I was sitting on a stump facing the ocean. I rocked my body forward and back, lengthening as I did so. I was very aware of a warm glow at the base of my spine. The warmth slowly grew and moved up my spine. My spine seemed to grow longer as the warmth moved up, filling me with a serene and peaceful glow. Finally it pushed through the base of my skull and out the top of my head. I do not know how long I lost myself in this experience.

My Eighth Session

The eighth session works on balance and the horizontal planes of the lower body. The focus is on the pelvic girdle.

I had this session done in Monterey on my way to Utah. I was in a bad mood and not happy about returning to Utah. When I told the Rolfer that I had just been accepted by Ida for training, he took this as a decree that I had to have a well-processed body. Ida was known for grading the work done on a person and would often call someone who did not meet her standards. Well, I resisted, and that poor Rolfer worked for over two hours. I felt beat. He did too, but he kept saying, "You have got to look right when you stand in front of Ida, and we only have two more sessions to go."

Anyway he finished and told me to spend the night at a motel before driving to Utah. No one ever tells me what to do so I drove for the next eighteen hours. I was really exhausted when I pulled up in Utah. I knew that I never wanted to be Rolfed again, and I did not care if I ever studied with Ida. I drove back to Esalen three days later, imbalanced and ungrounded. It was only months later when my body screamed to be worked that I made an appointment for the ninth session.

My Ninth Session

The ninth session works on balance and the horizontal and vertical planes of the upper body. It focuses on the shoulder girdle.

This session was very satisfying and more pleasant than any so far. My body was overripe, and every move the Rolfer made seemed to cause the structure to fall into place, to become balanced and whole, no longer just pieces that did not fit together. It was a real joy when I walked out feeling light and tall. I was glad that I had chosen to be Rolfed and happy that I had the chance to study with Ida.

My Tenth Session

The tenth session was a breeze. Rolfers say, "We just blow in your ear, pat you on the backside, and your tenth session is done." In this session the body is balanced and realigned in the final ways. The body is cleaned out physically, emotionally, and spiritually, and the person comes together on a higher level. I really felt that new high.

IDA ROLF

IDA HAD a Ph.D. in organic chemistry from Columbia University, had practiced yoga asanas extensively, and had also studied osteopathy and homeopathy before she developed her own method of working on the body. She had overcome considerable resistance and legal problems before winning recognition for the nature and value of her work. In her sixties she looked like a nice, little old grandma. But she was much broader and more powerful than she looked, and she loved fighting. I had listened to her in seminars before, but when I finally met her she was eating dinner in the Esalen Lodge with some friends.

I went to her table, knelt by her side, and introduced myself. "Dub Leigh!" she shouted, "I've heard all about you, how you're Rolfing people in your groups at the colleges and getting it written up in the school papers." I asked her how I could be Rolfing when I hadn't been trained.

She then accused me of giving her secretary a hard time and causing problems for her staff. I had insisted they let me talk to her about being trained even though they said I was too old, had no medical degree, and was in terrible shape myself. We were getting quite loud so we moved to the other end of the lodge where we would be alone. Our discussion got hotter and hotter. We began pointing fingers. Ida shook her fist at me. Then she stood up. I thought it was all over. I had blown my chances of ever learning Rolfing.

We stood there looking at each other. Then Ida said, "Let me see your hands." She took my hands in hers, studied them, looked into my eyes, and said, "Dub, I will make a Rolfer out of you." What follows are lessons and memories from my time with Ida.

It was my first lesson in my first class with Ida. I had memorized the recipe for the first Rolfing session. I was working the soft tissue

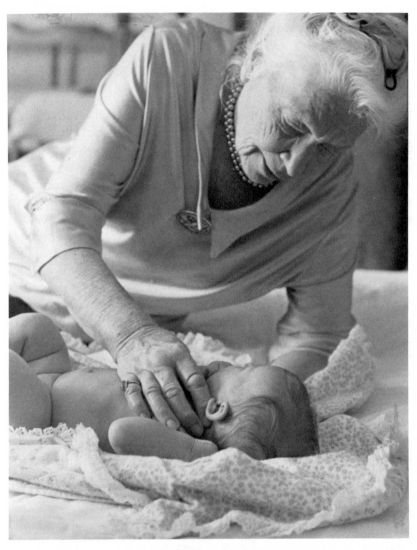

Ida working with a baby

of the chest, moving it headward and toward the midline. I felt the rib cage rise and expand. "Dub, what muscles are you working on?" Ida asked. I named the muscles. "And what are their origins and insertions?" she continued. I said I didn't know. She asked again, and again I said I didn't know. We went through this a third time. Then Ida turned to her assistant and asked him what I was doing in class when I could not answer these questions. He said that he guessed I shouldn't be in the class.

Something popped in me. My face got very red. I found myself reciting the muscles, their insertions and origins in a fast, strained, and unfamiliar voice. I skipped the insertion of the pectoralis minor and Ida picked it up right away. Without stopping, I shouted, "The spine of the scapula, the coracoid process." I was not sure I was right, but Ida said nothing more.

I finished processing my model and went out to the porch to unwind and let the ocean breeze dry my sweat. Another student followed me out, grinned all over, and said, "You sure blew your stupidity act this morning."

One of the women in the class suggested that my body would be better if I lost a few pounds. Ida disagreed. "He needs every pound he has," she said. "Who is going to process the two hundred pound bodies? He needs every pound to lean on those heavy people." Ida said that no Rolfer should work on a client who weighed more than him or her and that women Rolfers who are tiny should only process children.

"I would put Dub at the head of the endomorphs," Ida said. "Look at his body, sloping shoulders, big belly. He's all gut. A pure, 100% endomorph, a Buddha." She went on to explain how I would have stomach or lung diseases, not ailments of the nervous tissue or muscles which are associated with ectomorphs and mesomorphs respectively. Her last thought was that Rolfers who were mesomorphs would not destroy their body balance and alignment as quickly as endomorphs and ectomorphs of the same weight.

Ida was calling the shots from her rocking chair as three Rolfers worked on me. I had made up my mind that I would handle anything they could put out. I stayed with them, putting all my awareness under their fingers so pain was not a problem. After they finished, I went out on the porch and had a cup of tea. Half-way through the cup, I began to sob uncontrollably. Ida heard and brought me back into class where she worked on me for some time but could not ease the sobbing. She told a physician to take me to my motel room, lock me in, and take my car keys.

I was still weeping at the motel. I looked around the room and saw a plant that was also weeping. I got some water and poured it on the plant's soil, hoping that it would stop weeping. Then I got a can, climbed out a window, and dug up some rich soil, leaving a trail of tears wherever I went. I placed the soil around the plant, watered it, and the plant stopped crying. I got onto the bed, stretched out, and, fully clothed, slept twelve hours.

Again Ida was coaching three Rolfers working on me. She told them that no one had ever gotten into the base of my diaphragm, and she wanted it done here and now. I felt three pairs of hands go into my midsection as Ida cheered them on. Just as one of them got his hands under my ribs, Ida came over and pushed him away. She put her own hands and weight under my rib cage. I had never had anyone go that deep into my chest before, and I said to myself, "Let this little old lady in there." Then she took her hands out and told the other Rolfers to leave me alone.

Ida kept asking me what I felt and what thoughts had gone through my head as she sank her hands into me. It finally came out: "No son of a bitch can do anything to me unless I let him." Ida laughed and said that was my ground of being, the basic point of view from which I operated in life.

Ida told us not to worry about what our work might bring up in clients. Her instructions were to keep close and supportive but not to interfere in any way. She told us not to ask about personal matters, to let our clients talk if it served them, and to tell them that we wanted to hear only if this served them. Ida said our clients could handle anything they brought up. I have found this to be true.

Clients often release "poisons" in the process of being worked. These are toxins from past traumas; they make the eyes and nose water, leave a metallic taste on the tongue, and pollute the environment. Ida had this recipe for handling poisons:

18

1 large cast iron frying pan
1 insulated glove
¾ cup of Epsom salt
¾ cup of rubbing alcohol
1 box of matches

Pour the salt into the frying pan and level. Pour the alcohol onto the salt. Set the alcohol on fire. Put the glove on and carry the burning pan throughout the room. Make your movements clockwise. Have all windows and doors open during this process.

Ida also believed in cell salts. On the day she could not stop my weeping, she gave me four small white pills. They made me feel more grounded and helped me over my crying jag, so I asked what they were and where I could get them. With a straight face Ida said that an old lady scraped the salt from the top of a Montana cave and made the concoction. I volunteered to pick some up on my trips to Utah, but she did not respond.

A few years later while we drove from San Francisco to Big Sur, I found out the truth. Ida admitted pulling my leg and told me that the pills were "cell salts," more specifically potassium phosphate. She said that years ago they were illegal in the United States. She got her supply by going to Canada, letting the air out of her spare tire, and filling it with cell salts. She said cell salts balanced and stabilized the functioning of the brain and nervous system.

There was a chapter that didn't get into Ida's book on Rolfing. A woman in her early sixties, after five children and four sessions, recorded a ninety on the Kegel meter which measured the amount of pressure a woman could exert with the muscle tissue of her vagina. These readings indicated a woman's sexual ability or response. We could not believe our eyes. The young, well-built, great performers at Esalen only recorded forty or sixty. When this woman saw our astonishment, she told us that at Ida's suggestion she had been doing Dr. Kegel's exercises from the book *The Key to Feminine Response in Marriage* by Ronald M. Deutsch (New York, Random House, 1968).

Ida set up a research project in her first advanced class. Before-and-after-readings were taken on all the women models. Most of the before readings were in the twenties and thirties and the after

19

readings showed a gain of a few points to over twenty points. All of us were excited about the splash this information would make in the chapter on sex and the fourth session. But Ida was advised by a doctor that it would cause too much of a stir among the medical people. So the chapter was pulled, and the world was left without this information.

One day a doctor came into Ida's class, and after greeting her, asked if she had a student named "Dub." Ida said yes and pointed me out. The doctor said, "A patient of mine named Burley called me last night to complain of severe pain from a broken rib. He said that a big S.O.B. named 'Dub' had broken it in Ida's class earlier that day. He said that he could feel the end of the rib and had asked him to come over to help him with the pain."

Blood burned my face as I sat there in complete embarrassment. I knew Ida would throw me out now, and I would never become a Rolfer. I remembered how hard I had worked the day before in the area of his twelfth ribs, which had been buried down in his pelvis. My goal had been to dig them out and lift them headward so there would be space between the crest of the hip bone and the tip of the last rib. I felt I had done the left side well, but the right rib had not come free no matter how hard I worked and sweated. I could not remember anything snapping. Burley had groaned a lot, and I sweated a lot with Ida watching.

The doctor went on with the story, "When I got there, I felt the end of the rib that was painful. It was the end of the twelfth rib which had surfaced during the night. During his sleep, Burley had turned over and the rib came out from the crest of the hip bone. This movement had caused him great pain and wakened him. He felt the end of his twelfth rib for the first time in many years and was sure that Dub had broken it." Instead of being dismissed, I got a gold star.

When it came to teaching, Ida was a tough taskmaster. She sat for hours in her rocker and watched students fumble and muck through work that she could do in minutes. She told me that her toughest job was to hold herself in the rocker and watch.

On the last day of an advanced class, Ida was mercilessly berating one of the students for not going deep enough. She had been telling him for three months that his work was too superficial. The

20

poor guy just could not get the message. I guess Ida thought it was her last chance, and she was really heavy. Finally I could not stand it and blurted out, "I've had enough of this."

Ida spoke up quickly, "That goes for me, too. Look how nice it is outside."

I said, "By God, I can do something about it," and left. I was the only person I know of ever to walk out of Ida's class.

Ida said that it took a practitioner at least five years after his training to know what he was doing. She always ended a training by saying, "Now go out into the world and work, and may God protect both you and the public." Ida had considered at length the implications of sending new practitioners out to use her name and process bodies. She concluded that as inexperienced as they were, they would still give their clients value that they could not get elsewhere. She knew of no other practical way of training people. She wanted bodies processed and loved the Rolfer who turned out a lot of bodies week after week.

When Ida told me that she was setting up headquarters in Boulder, Colorado, she seemed irritated and somewhat upset. I was surprised and said that I could not imagine her in the winters of Colorado after all her years on the Big Sur coast. She shrugged, "What can I do?"

She had consulted two Los Angeles "sensitives," as she called them. They told her she should locate it in the Rocky Mountains. She did not like this and asked about any possibility of setting up the center on the West Coast. But they insisted that over the long haul, it had to be the Rocky Mountains. Ida then went to see Ann Armstrong, an old friend who is also a psychic. This time she asked, "Where on the West Coast should I set up my school?" Ann said, "Not the West Coast at all. Boulder, Colorado."

Ida shrugged again, "What can I do?" and asked me to help her move her records, books, and all the gear needed for classes to Boulder. I gathered it up, packed it into my station wagon, and hauled it to a friend's home in Boulder.

Seeing how much Ida trusted psychics made me curious, so I went to see her two Los Angeles sensitives. They said they would be glad to serve any friend of Ida. I asked where I fit into Rolfing. They said I had been married to Ida in seven different lifetimes.

Though we loved each other, we never did get along and this life-time would be no different. We would share much, but our work and lives would go in different directions.

Later that year Ida and I were in an *est* seminar together. During a break, she poked her finger in my midsection for emphasis and said, "I want you to be in my advanced Rolfing class this summer. You can be the first auditor ever." But Moshe Feldenkrais was start-ing his first American training that summer, and I was one of three people who had sent him the plane fare to come to the United States. I chose Moshe.

I didn't see Ida again until the end of the summer. She sent word for me to come and see her. She was still upset that I had spent the time with Moshe and not her. We battled back and forth. Others came to visit, picked up our vibrations, and quickly excused them-selves. Finally Ida asked, "If you love me the way you say you do, how can you hurt me the way you do?"

"We can only hurt those we love," I replied, feeling the truth of that old phrase. Tears came to Ida's eyes. I kissed her on the cheek. There were tears in my eyes too as I left and closed the door.

My love and association with Ida continued throughout the years. It was actually Ida who first told me of the work of Moshe Feldenkrais. She had met him in England, and they were friends throughout their lives. Ida always said that Moshe had taught her two very important things early in her career: 1. That emotions were tied into the muscles, and positive feelings were tied into the extensor muscles which have more white fiber than red, while neg-ative feelings were tied into the flexor muscles which have more red fiber. 2. That the posture of the body reflects the state of the mind.

Once she was coming down a hill at Esalen, and Moshe was going up. They were meeting for the first time in many, many years. They embraced for a few moments and then stepped back. Ida said, "Moshe, you need some work on your lower back."

Moshe answered, "Oh, no, Ida, it's my upper back."

On her eightieth birthday I suggested to Moshe that he write Ida a birthday letter. This is the letter he wrote:

Dear Ida,

Happy Birthday to you!

It gives me great pleasure to express on this occasion my admiration for your work and the feeling of love for your work and the feeling of love for your person.

We first met many years ago in Coomb Springs, Kensington, if my memory does not fail me, when Pak Subud came to England. You rolfed Mrs. Subud and one day you demonstrated your work to a large audience. I was in the theatre to see something that promised to be interesting.

You suddenly called my name and asked me to be your observer to tell to the audience what I saw you doing and to comment on it. You solved my puzzle of how you knew my name by referring to my earliest book. I was watching your marvelous performance and let you know that by asking to be rolfed by you. At the time, rolfing was not yet a verb, but your rolfing was a revealing and unforgettable experience for me.

Now that I am writing to you, I would like you to know that I know of few people of your intellectual integrity. I mean people who created something and do exactly what they say they are doing. You need not do more than you say, in as much as what you do is already extraordinary. Your teaching is as unique as your insight and your skill. Structural Integration and Functional Integration have more in common than the word that connects them. Indeed, in the case of humans, structure and function are meaningless, one without the other; so that *noleus voleus* when you integrate structure, as nobody else can, you improve functioning.

The sharpness of your intellect and your indefatigable spirit can age but never grow old. I hope I will be there on your 100th birthday to wish you good health for the future.

Your old friend and admirer,

Moshe Feldenkrais

FASCIA

We must see man as an energy field, rather than a mass of matter; a field which lives within a greater energy field, the field of the earth. In any competition the field of the earth will necessarily win. But realistically, in winning, the environment, the larger field, steadily undermines the integrity of the smaller field.

But fortunately there is a hopeful aspect in this rather grim situation. There is the happy possibility that we can restore the undermined structure, because incredibly, the human body is so outstandingly a plastic medium. As Rolfers we use this fact to great and unexpected advantage.[1]

Gravity, man's name for the energy of the earth, is the never-sleeping therapist and teacher. All we men and women as Rolfers can do is to prepare the body of the individual to receive and respond positively to the effects of the gravitational field. This is our sole contribution. And there is the message of structure.[2]

—Ida Rolf

IDA WAS unique in her focus on fascia. Fascia is the four dimensional web of elastic, connective tissue which envelops muscles, bones, organs, nerves, blood vessels. Fascia is what gives the body its shape. Ida called it the organ of structure. It is similar to the material that would be left if all the juice of an orange was removed. Fascia exists in layers of wrappings and webs throughout the body. It is formed into strings, belts, sheaths, cylinders, and so on.

Ida worked with this soft tissue jungle until it was aligned and organized with the earth's field of gravity so that the center of gravity of the body was lifted to its highest position when a person was standing. Ida called this structural integration. In the process, both tight, thick and brittle tissue as well as flaccid, stringy, and

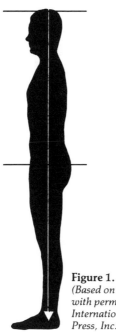

Figure 1.
(Based on original drawings with permission from International Universities Press, Inc.)

spongy tissue became toned and resilient. Tissue that was too cold or too hot returned to normal body temperature. Aches and pains went away; Ida called this a free lunch. The processed body seemed to take up more space; yet it seemed to weigh less and move with more grace and ease. The lift came from the body's energy field being aligned with the earth's.

Ideally the major segments of the body, the head, shoulders, thorax, pelvis, and legs, are in vertical alignment with the field of gravity. Both sides of the body are balanced, and the pelvis is horizontal so that the weight of the trunk falls directly over it. The spinal curve is small. The head rides above the spine, and the legs connect to it vertically, supporting the bottom of the pelvis. This ideal is represented in figure 1.

By the time a person is an adult, the body is usually far from ideal. There have been too many physical and emotional traumas. The body copes with such painful experiences by building body armor; it gets shorter, thicker, stiffer, tighter, bent out of shape in general. Throughout life, traumas and their compensations have a cumulative effect on the body, permanently aberrating the body's gravitational balance. "Aberration" comes from the Latin *aberrare*, which means to wander away from. Aberrations are distortions which cause the body to depart from the ideal, natural form. They can refer to structure that is misaligned, unsymmetrical, and imbalanced or to tissue that contains toxins or trauma.

For example, when a knee is twisted, a person limps for a few weeks until it is healed. During this time, weight is shifted to the strong leg, not only affecting the leg muscles, but also the muscles in the pelvis, spine, and shoulders. The rest of the body must adjust to the new demands. The limp eventually disappears, but the shoulders, pelvic girdle, and muscles throughout the body have been aberrated in varying degrees.

As an example of an emotional trauma leading to aberration, take this case of a young beautiful woman. I was working on the adductor muscles on the inside of her thighs in the fourth Rolfing session when she pushed me away and sat up with a peculiar, scared look on her face. She began shouting in a strained, fearful voice, "No! No! Stop! Not here! No, not now! This isn't the time! No we can't do that now! Please, no!" This went on for several minutes. Then a surprised look came over her face, then an embarrassed smile. The trauma of her first sexual encounter had remained locked in the tension in her thighs. When a traumatic incident is in the body, it creates aberration. When that incident is re-experienced and released, the aberration disappears.

Traumas are cataloged in "stacks." The older we get, the more stacks we have and the more traumatic incidents in each stack. Let's imagine you were born in a hospital and the doctor used instruments to deliver you. The left side of your head was bruised, and your left arm and shoulder were painfully folded. These pains are recorded together with all the other sensations you experienced at the time. The hospital smell, the bright lights, the noise of people talking, the paging system, the temperature of the room, the dryness and currents of the air, all were recorded as a complete package, filed away, and forgotten.

Some months later you are placed on a bathing table, and a rattle pokes you on the left side of the head. You have a sharp pain there, and your left arm and shoulder hurt. You see bright lights, smell hospital smells, hear people talking, and so on. You re-experience the original trauma and add the current experience to it.

When you are three, you fall off a tricycle and painfully twist your left arm and shoulder as you hit the ground. Your head hurts on the left side even though it was not touched, and again you re-experience sensations from your birth. This third incident is also recorded and neatly filed next to the second incident. As you get older, you notice that bright lights make your head hurt on the left and your left shoulder and arm feel uncomfortable.

Now at thirty-five you come to me for body work. I put my fingers into your left shoulder joint, and you have a lot of pain, not only in your shoulder, but also on the left side of your head. As I keep my fingers there, you experience the most recent trauma first. You see the tricycle fall and relive twisting your arm and shoulder. When this is processed, you may get back to the rattle and feel that same sharp pain in your head. If I stay in there with my fingers or go back in again, you may re-experience the original birth trauma. If you relive it completely, seeing the lights, smelling the hospital, hearing the people talking, and so on, you clean out the whole stack. You are freed of an entire series of traumas which were fixated in your body. Your body returns to a younger, more resilient state. You feel happier and more alive.

Besides traumas, badly learned patterns of movement also lead to aberrations throughout the body. Ida gives the example of walking.

If man weren't a standing, two-footed animal, he would have fewer problems. But he is standing, he is walking as best he can. He's been doing this since he was a kid—climbing up the side of his playpen and somehow getting his legs under him. Possibly he got his legs under him very badly, but he wasn't paying attention to that. He had one goal: he wanted to be like big brother, and big brother was able to walk. So, if he could get himself up against his playpen, and stand and take a step or two, he didn't care how he did it, he only cared that he did it. And he kept caring only that he did it, any old way. Presently, when he got to be a good deal taller and heavier, any old way wasn't good enough; but he didn't know that. Any old way disorganized his pelvis, disorganized his ribs, disorganized his head, disorganized the whole overlying structure.[3]

In a disorganized and aberrated body, the fascia in certain parts becomes rigid and stuck to itself or other tissues of the body. Ida said, "It's as though you have an overcoat with a safety pin holding the lining. Someone has pinned the lining to your coat, and it doesn't fit any more. So we are trying to take some of those safety pins of restriction out of the fascia envelope." She was willing to do whatever was necessary to free the fascia. It might be strumming a tendon as if it were a string on a violin, digging a muscle or tendon free from its neighbor with her fingernails, or poking her elbow in an armpit. Her goal was to release the aberrations in the fascia and free the natural structure of the body.

RELEASING FIXATIONS

TRAUMA suffered by a person has both physical and psychological consequences. Physical aberrations and psychological disorders are both symptoms of a person fixated by traumatic incidents. Rolfing releases the fixations in the fascia of the body and facilitates the release of psychological fixations by eliciting the experience of repressed emotions. I have seen the identity of the body and mind countless times on my table and offer the following cases as some examples.

The Most Poisonous Body

His was the most poisonous body I had ever worked. It was hard for me to realize that this clean-cut, all-American looking young man was releasing such unbelievably strong poison. My mouth tasted metallic, my nose rebelled, my body felt heavy, and the back of my head ached.

It was his first session and we were in a big attic room. When the situation became unbearable, I would go to the open window for fresh air and cleansing. I cough now as I think about it, just as I coughed then.

The whole hour went that way. I worked a little, got fresh air, and then did a little more work. At the end of the session, I was ill and went home. I showered and lay down. For three days, I was not well.

Later I asked this man about his background and found out that he had been a frogman during the Vietnam war, had been forced to kill people in hand to hand combat, and had been himself wounded on a number of occasions.

My Body Tells Me

I was working on the scarred area of Randy's shoulder. Years before a plane propeller had cut his chest, shoulder, and face. I was digging deep, trying to get the damaged tissue to lengthen and the shoulder to drop into a normal position.

As I worked, my eyes began to water and tears rolled down my cheeks. I was surprised and amazed, for I had no feeling or thoughts of grief. I was quite happy, yet here I was crying. Then I looked in the mirror and saw that tears were washing down both of Randy's cheeks.

This was the first time I found that my body told me where my client was emotionally. In fact, over the years I have found that sometimes I can feel their emotions before they do. I ask, "Are you sad?" They will reply at first, "No."

Then in a few moments they will say, "Yes, how did you know?" Now I feel the sadness, then wait a few moments and ask if they are sad. The answer is always yes, and sometimes they break out crying.

The Rug Cleaner Poison

The psychiatrist got up from the table coughing and choking. He walked toward the plants and opened the window for relief. I was coughing, too, as I left the room to wash the poison from my body.

Every time we worked, he gave out a poison that forced me to leave and him to go to the open window and plants. We would say that the people in the white coats would come for us if they knew how we were carrying on.

Certain areas of his body gave out very distinctive odors, and we named them. The "rug cleaner" was one of the strongest and most distinct. After one session when the "rug cleaner" smell flowed, the psychiatrist went directly from my office to a meeting. The people in the room began sniffing and commenting on the odor. Someone said she thought the carpet had just been cleaned.

We found that people could pick up the smells in the hallway outside my work room. As time went on, we found we could see the poison coming from his body. It was then that we got worried again about our own sanity. We brought another person into our room to share the secret, and she had the same experience.

The plants loved the poison and dissipated it from our sight and smell as the psychiatrist stood near them and rubbed his back against them. We also found that spraying a mist of water also helped to clean the air.

The Blue Man

I started to work on this middle-aged man, when I noticed that he was starting to turn blue. I stopped working and asked him if this had ever happened before. He said that he had gone to three other Rolfers and that each one had gotten scared and stopped when he started to turn blue.

We talked for awhile, and he assured me that he would take the responsibility should he die on my table. He even wrote a note to that effect.

I worked him through the blue sessions, slowly and gently. Toward the end of his ten sessions, there was no more blueness.

Did he get changes? He snapped out of a long depression, quit the job he had had for twenty years, divorced a wife he had been with for about twenty-five years, left the U.S., and started a new life in a different field in a different country.

The Sit-Up Phenomenon

He said he was the sit-up champion of the state. He had been in training for over one year, and during that period of time he had lost one and a half inches in height. He was built like a pregnant fireplug, and his back pained him. He could not sleep nights, and his coach had the same problems.

I found that his abdomen was as hard as a rock and that the back matched the front. I asked him to lie down and do a sit-up while I held the muscles in the front of the abdomen and the muscles in the small of the back (lumbar area). He could see how both sets of muscles—both front and back—fired and shortened at the same time.

Then I had him look at where these muscles were attached and what he did to himself when he shortened both his front and his back at the same time. The spine had to shorten and move forward, making a greater curve in the lower back and crushing the spinal discs. His upper spine then had to change to balance the lower back curve.

I worked his tight, short muscles until they softened and lengthened. The spine got longer, he got taller.

That night, he got a good restful sleep for the first time in months.

The 200-Pound Baby

He was an employee of the I.R.S. and weighed well over 200 pounds. As I went deeper into his tissues, he began to sob. They were not the normal sobs you would expect from a man experiencing emotional trauma, but the pitiful sobs of a young infant—loud and strong, as if he were in extreme pain. He brought his feet up over his chest and held them like a baby as he cried. This intense sobbing had happened before, and he always brought his body into the fetal position, just as a baby does.

I knew he was unaware of my presence, and I needed to use the bathroom, so I left him sobbing and went up the hall. I could hear the weeping very clearly in the waiting room, and the two women there seemed very upset. Finally, one said, "What on earth are they doing to that baby?" I told them that that baby was a mature man.

They waited and watched and, sure enough, a 200-pound man came out of the room with a soft face and red eyes.

Ear Pain in the Toes

I worked my thumb into the fleshy part of the last two toes. The young medical doctor from Los Angeles squirmed with pain and finally pulled her foot away from me. I asked her to allow me to work deeply again and to look as I did so to see if there were some old trauma attached to or hidden in her toes.

As I worked, she squirmed, groaned, and in a young girlish voice screamed, "No, mother, no, please don't." Then she began weeping. I eased up on her toes and put my hand over hers as she wept. When the weeping stopped, she sat up and said, "My mother would pour hot oil into my ear when I had an earache."

32

Since her mother had poured oil in both ears, I suggested we try the other foot. As I worked the toes on the other foot, she again screamed for her mother to stop and began weeping.

When the weeping was finished, we again worked both sets of toes; there was no pain.

Witchcraft

She took hold of my hand with both of hers and frantically, hysterically jerked it away from her. I had been doing the seventh session work in her mouth and was working on the muscles under her tongue.

I pulled back and watched her fear and pain as she contracted her body and rolled from side to side, moaning and groaning in a very strange voice. Then she lay still—too still. At the time, I was a new, green Rolfer. Nothing like this had ever happened to me, and I wasn't prepared for it. God, what had happened? What was going on? What had I done? What should I do?

I called her by name and asked how she felt. I asked if she could hear me. No response. I felt helpless, at a complete loss about what to do. I tried again to talk to her, to get some response by touching her. She just lay there, limp and lifeless.

We were at a ski resort. I put on my shoes and coat and went out into the snow and walked up and down the road for awhile, thinking. What would I do if she never came back? I would have to call a doctor friend from town and have him come up and take over.

When I returned to the room, she was lying just as I had left her. I sat on the side of the bed and picked up her limp hand. I began to cry as I talked to her, pleading with her to come back to life. Slowly, she started to move, and it was some minutes before she spoke. Then she told me this story.

She was in Boston, Massachusetts, and she gave me the exact date. She had been tied to a stake as a witch, and her tongue had been cut out.

The Return from Drowning

I was working the shoulder of an internationally famous woman when she began to cough and jerk. This slowly worsened until she was flailing her arms, coughing, choking, trying to vomit and jerking convulsively, especially with her legs and pelvis. I tried to get hold of her neck as a means of support, but she moved and jerked too much for me to hold her. I moved to the side of the table and placed my right hand on her abdomen, just above the navel, in an attempt to center her from this area and keep her on the table.

It seemed quite a long time before she began to quiet down and slowly stop the choking. The waves of jerking continued, especially the right side, but became less severe and frequent. Finally, she lay quiet and still. Her mouth was partly open, and the quietness became so intense that I could not detect any breathing.

I began talking to her, calling her by name and asking, then ordering, her to come back. Slowly the breathing became discernible, and after a time, she opened her eyes and said she had gone away. Then I felt the room being flooded with grief. I asked her if she felt any sadness and she began to sob, "No one would help me, no one would save me. They just stayed there on the bank and watched me drown."

We held each other closely as she sobbed. Tears welled up and rolled down my cheeks. I was glad my head was turned so she couldn't see. After what seemed like a long time, she got up, walked over and started to put her clothes on. I went to the restroom to compose myself.

She hardly said anything until I saw her out the door. There she stopped, hugged me, and told me simply that she loved me. Then she said, "I have been told how beautiful it is to die and how hard it is to come back, and it is true."

Ski-Racing at Eight Months

At the encouragement of her husband, a medical doctor, she came to me because of her painful back. Her lower back was so far forward and her buttocks were so high up, you could hang your hat on either cheek. We got the back flat, the buttocks down closer to the ground, and the pain gone. Then she became pregnant.

We worked to keep her body loose, the baby's space unconstricted, and the new weight back over the pelvis and legs. Every month we would loosen what had tightened, always working to keep the back flat and as erect as possible.

She kept up her skiing, and during her eighth month she entered a cross-country ski race, competing against high school and college kids. She won and then delivered the baby with no problem.

I was in Salt Lake City a few days after she returned home with the baby. She asked me to work on her, and I told her it was too soon. Her husband set an appointment for himself at 7:30 the next morning.

When I answered the door at 7:30, she was there, smiling, and said she'd awakened her husband during the night and asked him to relinquish his appointment to her. We put the stuff back to where it used to be, lengthened and straightened her back, and she went away light and happy.

The Painful Coccyx

She was in her last trimester, and her pregnancy had been quite free of pain until the coccyx area of her pelvis began to give her constant pain. I had worked her once each month, and the baby was over the pelvis. All seemed well except for the new pain.

I worked her everywhere but was careful to stay away from the coccyx area. The problem persisted. I did not like the idea of working the coccyx area this late in a pregnancy. We talked it over, and she said for me to go ahead.

I found a little string of fascia tying the coccyx to the right leg. With work, the string disappeared and the coccyx was free and floating. The pain was gone too. The mother thanked me, and I feel the baby would have too if he could.

The Computer Programmer

He walked around the room, sat down on the table for a few seconds, stretched his arms, got up and paced around again. Together we got his clothes off except for his shorts, and finally he lay down on the table, only to jump up and pace around the room again.

He had contracted to write a computer program. The time was about up, and the work was nowhere near finished. My job was to get him sane so he could get it done by the coming Thursday. At first, I followed him around, trying to work his neck. When he landed on the table, I would quickly work the big extensor muscles of his back. Little by little he calmed down, and finally he stayed on the table. For over two hours I worked the extensor muscles, getting them relaxed, soft and long. When he got up and left, I believe he was more sane and more grounded than I was.

Thursday afternoon, he came back to pay me. He told me that he had finished his contract and gotten his money.

A Pop in the Neck

My friend was over his desk, really sick. I was a freshman Rolfer and was visiting him in the governor's office after returning to Utah. He grumbled about how well I looked and asked what I was doing in California. I told him I was Rolfing, and he wanted to know what that was, so I offered to let him experience it.

I had him take off all his clothes except his shorts, and we went to work. It was quite a show. Secretaries popped in, screamed and backed out. No one lingered or stopped to watch. I found something strange going on in one side of his neck. As I turned his head, something seemed to constrict the movement. I was putting quite a lot of pressure on the side of his neck and turning his head at the same time, when something popped. It sounded almost like a gunshot, and his head flopped around on the side that had been constricted. God, I was sure I had broken something, right under my hand.

When I had collected myself, I asked him how he felt and had him move his head from side to side. Everything seemed okay and normal now. He dressed and went back to work feeling much better, and I went back to my hotel to worry. The next morning, I called him nervously. He was fine and has retained the extended movement ever since.

Work the Foot and Fix the Shoulder

He was the first man to ever Rolf me, and now he had come to me to be Rolfed. I felt honored. He said he'd hurt his right shoulder in a fall, and he wanted to get rid of the chronic pain.

As he stood in his jockey shorts, what seemed most aberrated were his feet and his right shoulder. I told him that his feet needed a lot of work. He agreed, but he wanted me to work on his painful shoulder. I could not stay away from his poor feet and told him that I wanted to start there and then go to the shoulder. He did not like the idea at all but agreed.

I really got into working his poor painful feet, and he was doing a lot of moaning as the hour passed. Finally, when the hour was about gone, I stood him up to try out his new feet, and he seemed quite pleased as he walked around the room. He liked the way his feet and legs moved. He said they were more like hands. I asked him how his shoulder was. With a surprised, puzzled grin he said he could find no pain as he went through the various shoulder movements.

Insurance Payments

Her right hand was like a frozen claw, and the thumb could not come close to touching any of the fingers. She had come with her husband and was not a client. I noticed her hand after I had finished working him. I asked her if I could see her hand and maybe work it. So, while he dressed, I worked her hand. Working the fingers was very painful for her, but when we finished the thumb could touch all the fingers. I was proud and happy and not very observant.

I told her that if she would come with her husband, I would work on her hand while he was dressing, at no cost to her, and I felt sure that her hand would continue to get better.

She did not come with him again. I always asked about her. Finally, he told me that she would not come because she was afraid she would lose her insurance payments.

Stroke Symptoms for Sympathy

She had all the symptoms of a stroke patient. I would work her, and we would get movement that she had not had before—more range, more freedom. I would see her go, feeling good about our accomplishments; then the next week I could see the all our improvement had vanished. I stopped charging her for my work, called her husband, and asked if he could see any change.

He said she seemed to walk and talk better when she didn't know anyone was around. I called the doctor who had referred her, and he said that when he pressed her, she admitted that she

37

was ill because she wanted to be ill and have her husband and children take care of her.

The Pain in the Neck

We had just finished his tenth session, and as he walked around, I asked him what he had gotten out of his Rolfing. He put that studied look on his face for a few minutes and then he said, "You Know, Dub, I can't really think of a thing I can point out as an improvement." I was shocked, very upset, and I said nothing as he dressed, paid me, and left.

Then I looked at the picture taken before the first session and the picture taken after the tenth. It was clear that his head had moved three or more inches back over his body and that his neck and body were longer and thinner.

Then I looked at his card. He had come in complaining about chronic neck pain and was taking cortisone shots to dull the pain. He stopped taking those shots after the fifth session and had no pain.

About a year later, I ran into this doctor on the street and asked him how he was. He told me his neck was still paining him. He said, "I just didn't get anything out of my Rolfing." He was back taking cortisone shots. His body reverted because I had failed to help him develop the awareness of the changes. I feel I failed in part because he could not believe that anyone out of the medical field could really help his condition.

Kissing a Stranger

As I worked her neck, I was flooded with a feeling of warmth and love for this woman whom I hardly knew. There was a feeling of serenity and oneness. I could not discover where my hands stopped and where her body began. I became more and more lost in an all-encompassing oneness. Then I completely went away. Nothing existed.

I was suddenly brought back by a knocking on my office door. I got up, walked to the door, opened it, embraced the woman who was standing there, and kissed her softly and warmly on the mouth. I told her I would be finished in a few minutes and asked her to wait in the waiting room. I went back into my office, closed the door, sat down on my stool and continued my work on the client's neck.

Then the thought struck me, "I've never seen that woman before!" I jumped up and hurried to the door and found she was still standing there. I was embarrassed as I apologized for my actions.

She answered simply, "It did seem like the right thing to do."

The Back Operation

She took a breath, then sighed deeply, and said she was without pain for the first time in years. She and her husband had stopped off at my office on their way to the airport from Marin County.

Her husband was a client, and he had insisted that his wife get her first session from me before catching the plane for New York and her scheduled back operation. The wife took the plane, but when she got to the hospital, she reported that she had experienced no pain since leaving my office. The doctors canceled the operation, and she flew home.

I completed a series of ten sessions, and then she became pregnant. I worked her through her pregnancy. Her back handled the extra weight with no unnatural discomfort.

Getting Taller

He was one of those tall ectomorphs—long, skinny legs, high, coat-hanger shoulders—and not much meat to work with. He loved running, and it was a major part of his life.

There was a lot of pain for us to work through, and although he seemed able to run through the pain of marathon training, he was not particularly willing to work through it on the table.

His first session was a real problem for us both. I had trouble doing my job, and he had trouble handling the discomfort that kept coming up. He was up, off the table, and pacing around the room a large part of the time. We finally got finished, and I told him that I could not do him much good. I suggested that he go somewhere else for his body work. He did not seem too put out as we shook hands, for the last time I hoped, and he left.

Later that day, he called me up and wanted to set up another appointment. I told him I did not want to work him and asked him why, after such an ordeal, he wanted to continue. He said, "I just measured myself and I gained two inches in height since you worked on me."

Getting into a Rut

I was in my office talking on the phone when a knock came on the door of my adjoining workroom. Since it was time for my two o'clock appointment, I called, "Come right in, take your clothes off and lie down on your back. I'll be right in."

Moments later I hung up the phone and walked into my workroom to find a strange female standing there in shock.

Werner Erhard

After Ida was introduced to Werner Erhard, the founder of *est*, she looked him over, then turned to me and asked, "Is he a Rolf junkie?" As I laughed and nodded, she asked, "Why didn't you put his ears on right?"

Later, when we were alone, Ida said that I had over-stretched the hip joint ligaments. After talking about it, we concluded that Werner's habit of sitting with one leg bent back under him was the real culprit.

I made up a slightly upholstered board to put on his canvas campaign chair, knowing that the hard seat would make it uncomfortable for him to sit on his leg. He still sits on his legs, and I don't know where my board is.

The Family with Almost No Pain

She was a beautiful, sensitive woman whom I liked from the beginning, but she experienced pain whenever I pressed my fingers into her flesh. It was evident that she was going to have a tough time getting through the ten sessions.

I stopped the pressure and started talking. "Can you tell me how many fingers I have on your rib cage? Can you separate the two hands? Can you tell me what direction my fingers are moving? Am I lifting your tissue? Now take a deep breath. How does that change what you experience? Now can you feel that bone? Can you feel how the muscle is attached? What am I doing? Can you feel how it is moving? Now move your elbow straight out and straight in slowly. What do you experience in your chest? Now breathe deeply again and see the difference."

"Now did that hurt?" I asked.

She answered, "No," and laughed. The mind can only focus on one thing at a time; by completely attending to what was happening she had bypassed the pain.

From then on she and her whole family travelled to San Francisco to have the painless Rolfer work on their bodies. There was one exception—her husband. He was an extremely successful businessman who truly excelled. He was a fine man, an achiever, a pusher. Looking inside himself and meditating were not his bag.

As I pushed with my fingers, attempting to get into his tissue, I could feel his tissue pushing back. We were pushing against each other, and he experienced pain. If I pushed harder, he pushed back harder to keep me out. Neither of us could win. I love the man, I respect the man, but I could not get my job done with him.

The Big Husband and the Fragile Wife

Jim explained how he wanted to be Rolfed and knew he would have no problem with pain. He said, however, that his wife Alice was very sensitive to pain. She had been raised with a silver spoon in her mouth, never had a problem or an unpleasant, painful experience in her life, and probably would have trouble. Jim let me know he had excelled in sports in and out of college and was also a successful self-made businessman. Well, Jim squirmed, groaned, and limped through five sessions before he cried, "Enough," and quit, which was fine with me.

Alice, on the other hand, was a pure joy. From the first moment, I could take my fingers through her connective tissue without any sign of resistance. She had no pain whatsoever. At the finish of each session she would ask why I didn't do the same things with her that I did with Jim. At the beginning of the next session she insisted that I work her body as I did Jim's. I have a feeling that to this day she believes that I did not work her and Jim with the same intensity.

The difference was not in what I did; it was in what each of

41

them did. I feel that one looked and allowed and the other pro-
grammed pain and resisted.

The All-Pro

Ted gave me a push that sent me across the room. Then he rolled
to his feet and, with fists clenched, paced the room cussing out a
player whom he called by name, telling me how this guy had hit
him on the blind side. They had carried Ted off the football field.

His face, his body, his voice were really into reliving that incident in his life. Slowly, he let go of the pain and emotion and
finally lay back down on my table.

I put my elbow back into the same spot in his hip and had him
move his knee back and forth. The unbearable pain and trauma
were gone. It was now moving as a normal hip joint should move.

FUNCTIONAL INTEGRATION
AND AWARENESS
THROUGH MOVEMENT

MOSHE FELDENKRAIS

MOSHE was born in Russian-occupied Poland in 1904. At around fourteen he went to Israel on his own and worked building houses for ten years. Though he was not formally educated, he translated a book on auto-suggestion before leaving to study at the Sorbonne in Paris. There he earned his D.Sc. in applied physics. His thesis involved the development of the instrument that he and his colleague used for the first fission experiments.

After Moshe fled from France to Britain in World War II, he joined the British Admiralty and participated in submarine detection research. During this time, doctors recommended he operate on the knee he had injured playing soccer as a young man. They only gave him a fifty-fifty chance of walking normally again, however. So after the war, he set aside his career as a physicist and devoted himself to the study of movement and awareness. He conducted exhausting studies in neuroanatomy, yoga, Eastern philosophies, and Gurdjieff. At thirty-two he became the first European to earn a black belt in Judo. He founded the first Judo club in France and wrote several popular books on the subject. Eventually he restored his knee to full functioning and developed his own methods of enhancing movement and awareness in others.

Moshe spoke several languages and was a renowned teacher in Israel, France, Denmark, Germany, Switzerland, and the United States. He authored numerous books including *The Case of Nora, Body and Mature Behavior, Awareness Through Movement, Judo, Higher Judo, The Potent Self,* and *The Elusive Obvious.*

Moshe's desire for knowledge was insatiable. He wanted to learn what everyone else was doing, then show the world that what Moshe Feldenkrais did was the finest. He loved to have people around him tell him how great his work was. It seemed that he always had to be at the center of the stage. I never figured out whether he really had a terrible temper or if he just liked to be dramatic. When someone attacked or even questioned his work, he went wild. He drowned out his opposition with his hollering. He thought that someday he would be a great actor.

His physical presence was immense. He made it a habit of sizing up men as opponents and women as companions. But when it came to children, he was a softie. The love, understanding, and fun between Moshe and his young clients were boundless and a joy to see.

I first met Moshe at Esalen in 1972. He and Will Schutz were heading towards a narrow gate from one side, and I was coming from the other. We reached the gate at the same time, stopped, and faced off. We just stood there, saying nothing. I had the feeling he was measuring me for a fight, and the thought flashed through my mind, "I can take this old codger." Finally Will came up, introduced us, and suggested we all go to his house.

It was my first class with Moshe. "Everyone, stop!" Moshe cried suddenly. "Except that fellow there." He pointed to me and said, "You just keep doing what you're doing."

With about ten other people, I was lying on my stomach, following his instructions to bend the knees at right angles to the floor and to bend the feet at right angles to the lower legs, so that the soles of the feet would be parallel to the floor.

"Just look at his feet," Moshe said. "They are not parallel to the floor. His feet and toes point toward the ceiling. And he thinks they are flat, at right angles to his lower leg. Now how can a body worker know what he is doing when he doesn't even know where his own feet are?"

Then he proceeded to give me specific instructions on how to move the feet back and forth, up and down, until my feet were parallel to the floor after several minutes. Finally he turned from me and finished his lesson with the whole class.

I walked out burning with humiliation and embarrassment and headed for my room. My roommate found me throwing things angrily into my suitcase. "What's going on?" he asked.

"I'm through!" I exploded. "That man has no common decency or respect for other people. I'm sorry I helped pay his way to come here. I'm leaving."

The next morning I was at the front desk waiting to turn in my room key when I felt an arm around my shoulder. It was Moshe. "Come on," he said, "let's go back to class." I did, and I'm glad.

Moshe's famous bad knee had been troubling him for days. Some of the better bodyworkers at Esalen had worked on it without success. Moshe told us the story about how the same thing had happened in Tel Aviv years ago. His advanced students back then worked on his knee one after another. But it got worse instead of better, so finally he told them, "I'll go home and fix it myself."

The next day Moshe jumped into the air and slapped his formerly painful knee. Of course the amazed class wanted to know how he had done it, and of course, Moshe would not tell them. Some months later after he had been partying, they got the secret out of him. He told them, "I talk to it," and showed them the intricate maneuvers he took his knee through.

He spoke to his knee as if it were a sick person distinct from himself. "Yes, we can move it a little here; fine; okay; no, all right we won't do that. Yes, okay here. Easy now. Okay. No, not that." And so on, slowly moving his injured knee as he put his body in every conceivable position. He played around with it until the painful area got smaller or disappeared in each of the various positions.

"As soon as I had complete awareness in my knee joint," Moshe said, "I had no pain in it." Through the years, he has kept his knee functioning in this way.

One by one Moshe had us lie on the table on our backs, arms at the sides, while the rest of the class looked on. Then he asked us what we had seen. We made observations and guesses until Moshe announced, "The powerful people are those who lie with their elbows out and palms down." Those who lie with their arms any other way are not able to get the power of the pelvis through the shoulder and elbow; their power 'mushes out' and is dissipated."

"I disagree," called out Pritchard, a Rolfer. "I don't think the point of the elbow should go straight like that."

Being a Rolfer too, I spoke up, "Pritchard, even Ida says the same thing."

Pritchard turned to me, "Then they are both wrong."

Moshe turned livid and sputtered, "Everyone, lie down on your back on the floor!"

For three days, our Awareness through Movement lessons consisted of nothing but arm, shoulder, wrist, and finger movements. Moshe gave no lecture and took no questions. There was just work, work, and more work. No rest for our upper girdles. Hour after hour we twisted, rotated, and lifted out arms in every conceivable position. I muttered to a classmate, "By the time we're finished, we'll have worked out everything there could be to work out in our upper bodies."

At the end of the third day, Moshe asked Pritchard to stand by him as each student walked past. "You see," crowed Moshe, "how every single arm here hangs with the thumb next to the leg and the point of the elbow out." After three days all of us, even Pritchard, proved Moshe right.

Moshe's work at Esalen was so successful that he was invited to do workshops around the country. I decided to follow him. One day in our training in San Francisco, Moshe was acting cantankerous, and he knew it. "What I need," he said, "is a young woman with dimples in her cheeks to take care of me," and he laughed and laughed. I laughed, too. I knew what he meant because I had read the chapter on "Muscular Habit and the Sexual Act" in his book *Body and Mature Behavior*.

A few days later a nice young lady arrived from Israel to take care of his household needs, and Moshe was again his happy, congenial self.

The cheeks with dimples were not on the face. Dimples in the pelvic cheeks indicate the ability to move the pelvis as needed for full orgasm.

On another occasion one of the students accused Moshe of holding back information and techniques he could teach us if he chose to. Of course, he was insulted and put on quite a show. I did not think much of it at the time, but after many years of work and exposure to other schools, I believe Moshe did hold back. I can remember seeing him put nerves back in his individual work. I did not know what he was doing, and he did not explain. This skill has been practiced in the martial arts for hundreds of years, and my guess is that Moshe learned it from his Judo teachers. Moshe did whatever he had to to get the job done: joint manipulation, changing the self-image through words, or maybe trigger point work.

Moshe went to Vancouver, Canada, to work with the elderly, and he did a seminar in the biggest ballroom I had ever seen him work in. He was doing one of those lessons in which the legs and trunk form a "v." I did not like folding my chubby belly, and I was as far away from him as I could get in a corner of the room.

I worked at the movement for a few minutes on the floor; then I got up in disgust and found a seat by the wall. I sat there and did the movements in my imagination. After a while I returned to the floor and did the movement physically for a few minutes. Then I went back to the chair and did them in my head. I continued this pattern throughout the evening, thinking that Moshe couldn't see me.

But toward the end of the class, Moshe blew my anonymity completely. "You see that fellow down there in the corner," he asked, pointing straight at me, "the one in the white shirt who's been bobbing up and down all night? Well, he has gotten more out of this workshop than anyone else. Look how well he does the movement now, and most of the hard work he did in his imagination!" I felt like the belle of Canada's largest ball.

I introduced Moshe to Werner Erhard, and once I watched while Moshe worked on Werner's feet. He talked as he worked and often needed two hands to get his point across. So by the time Moshe finished the right foot, the allotted forty-five minutes were gone, and the left foot had not been touched.

When I saw Moshe finishing up, I suggested he use my appointment to finish Werner's other foot. Moshe answered, "Werner can do his other foot himself in his head."

"But, Moshe, you can use my time to finish his other foot," I insisted.

Moshe turned to me in disgust and said, "You just lost your time." Werner and I both went home.

During the summer of 1980, Moshe taught his last advanced training in San Francisco. An old Israeli friend and teacher of Moshe's, Elie Fabian, was my house guest during this time. Moshe invited him to sit in on the training as his special guest. One day Moshe told one of his long, detailed, often-humorous stories. As he related the story, Elie kept poking me with his elbow saying, "That isn't the way it was. I was there."

After the session was over, Elie recounted the event as he had experienced it and said that he would straighten Moshe's memory out at the first opportunity.

Moshe's reply was, "It doesn't matter. No matter!" He explained, as he had so many times, that his students would soon forget the details of what he had talked about in the morning. What they would remember was the story and the point the story made. That was the way Moshe taught and his students learned, no matter if the story was a little fabricated.

Moshe teaching the Feldenkrais Method,
Lone Mountain College, 1976

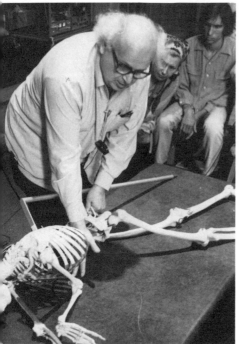

MOVEMENT AND AWARENESS

Man is an animal because of his structure. But he is the highest animal and a human being because of the functioning of his nervous system. The hand of man differs only slightly from that of an ape—in the position and movement of the thumb—but the nervous system of man allows him to use the muscles and bones of his hand to do what anthropoid ape cannot do: the fine, manipulative, specifically human movements such as writing, playing an instrument, counting bank notes, repairing a watch, or focusing a microscope.[1]

—Moshe Feldenkrais

THE HUMAN SPECIES is molded by instinct far less than any other animal species. We are unique because our nervous system is not wired in at birth. For the greater part we acquire our habits as we go. The calf drops from the cow clothed in fur, stands, finds a teat, and starts sucking. The human baby is born naked and helpless. It can only cry and flail about when its needs are not met. Animals are born completely wired with most of the patterns they will use during their entire lifetimes, and their brain size changes very little. Humans are born with the most complex and sophisticated nervous systems but with only one reflex operational at birth, the falling instinct which causes the baby to contract when dropped. We learn most of the patterns we need to survive, and at maturity our brains are five times larger than at birth. Compared with animals we have an infinite capacity to learn different patterns of behavior. The sophistication of our nervous system makes self-awareness and muscular refinement possible to a remarkable

52

degree. We have the possibility of living gracefully in full awareness.

If our nervous system ultimately gives us an advantage over animals, it also allows us to learn inefficient, aberrated patterns. To perform the simple act of sitting, for example, we rarely align our structure and allow gravity to support us. Instead we clench our thigh muscles, strain our back, constrict our breathing, push our neck forward, and so on, eventually impairing not only our motor activity but our thoughts and feelings as well.

What we wire into our nervous systems are not separate patterns of movement, thought, and feeling, but entire experiences. The self records the movements, thoughts, and feelings of an experience as a whole. They are inseparable, and changes in any are reflected in changes in all.

Feldenkrais focused on changing maladaptive patterns by bringing into awareness the motor components of undesired behavior. He maintained that motor activity was essential for any behavior, not only observable physical movements but even for thought and feelings and even consciousness itself. The following references are excerpted from two lectures Feldenkrais gave at the Copenhagen Congress of Functional Movement and Relaxation in the early 1970's.

My contention is that the unity of mind and body is an objective reality, that they are not entities related to each other in one fashion or another, but an inseparable whole while functioning. To put this point more clearly, I contend that a brain without motor functions could not think or at least that the continuity of mental functions is assured by corresponding motor functions.

Let me substantiate this point by some striking examples: a. It takes us longer to think the number from twenty to thirty than from one to ten, though the numerical intervals are the same from 1–10 and 20–30. The difference lies in the fact that the time intervals are proportional to the time needed to utter the corresponding numbers aloud. This suggests that we actually mobilize the brain mechanism of the vocal apparatus. . . . b. In counting objects we find, in general, the linkage of the motor parts of vision and verbalization keeping down the speed of thought to the rate of the motor elements. c. Most people cannot think clearly without mobilizing the motor function of the brain enough to become aware of the word patterns representing the thought. . . . These examples indicate that an improvement in speed and clarity of thought may be obtained by reducing the extent of movement and smoothing the performance of the muscular controls.

We have no sensation of the inner workings of the central nervous system; we can feel their manifestations only as far as the eye, the vocal apparatus, the facial mobilization and the rest of the soma provoke our awareness. This is the state of consciousness!

Let us consider feeling in more detail. a. I am buoyant, my breath even, my face at the point of smiling. I feel gay. My motor attitude is quite different when I feel disgusted. Then my face is like that of a man on the brink of or immediately after vomiting. b. I clench my lower jaw; my fists and breath are held; my pulse is accelerated; my eyes and head move in jerks, and my neck is stiff. I am angry and on the verge of hurting, but I am trying not to let myself go. . . . There is usually a clear motor pattern sufficient even for an objective evaluation of the intensity of feelings.

Not only individual development or abnormality can be followed through the soma but even wider cultural and racial attitudinal differences, such as the introversion, the non-attachment, the indifference of the Hindu and the looseness of his hip joints; and the extroverted, clinging, holding-on, time-is-money attitude of the industrial nations with their utter inability to sit cross-legged. And, of course, to soften and bring to normal one's hip joints, one must spend time looking at oneself and giving up attachments.

The advantage of approaching the unity of mental and muscular life through the soma lies in the fact that the muscular expression is simpler. It is concrete and simple to locate. It is also incomparably easier to make a person aware of what is happening and therefore yields faster and more direct results.[2]

Feldenkrais had two basic, broad ideals guiding his work: 1. Movement should be limited by the skeletal structure and not the musculature. 2. Action should be done gracefully with maximum efficiency. He wrote:

The head movements must have no predilection for particular directions. The "normal" head should have easy access to all directions of the anatomically possible range. The limiting factor should be the skeletal structure and not the muscular impediments. It can be shown that every adult uses only a part of the theoretical possibilities of the human frame.

The healthy coordinated movements of the body as a whole obey the mechanical principle of least action, while the muscles work in step and perform their task with the least expenditure of metabolic energy. In view of these principles governing the operations of the whole human frame one can decide on normal and abnormal behavior.[3]

Feldenkrais called his individual work Functional Integration and his group work Awareness through Movement. He sought to teach clients to become aware of what they were doing. He often said, "If you don't know what you are doing, you certainly can't do what you want to do." In his individual work, in addition to exercises in movement and awareness, Feldenkrais used his hands to create new awareness in the nervous system. He described his individual work briefly as follows:

I never deal with the affected member or articulation before an improvement in the head-neck relationship and the breathing has been brought about. This, in turn, cannot be achieved without a betterment of the spine and thorax configuration. Again the pelvis and abdomen must be corrected. In practice the procedure is a successive series of approximations, each one allowing a further improvement in the segment just dealt with.

I insist on thirty to forty sessions at a daily rate and ten twice or three times a week until the major complaint is gone. Normally, that is in about fifty percent of the cases, pains and inability to use a member disappear before the daily sessions are over. . . . In due course I go through thirty different situations up to sitting, standing, walking, and balancing on two wooden rollers.[4]

One of Moshe's techniques was to go with aberrations until they released. Some aberrations occur when two antagonistic muscles or muscle groups oppose each other rather than cooperate. Moshe would exaggerate the aberration, forcing the dominant muscle to relax since he was doing its work and stretching the inferior muscle and rejuvenating it with a new, fresh flow of blood. Take, for example, his work on scoliosis, a lateral curve in the spine. In scoliosis one psoas muscle is skinny and stringy with poor muscle tone. It is far too long in comparison with the other psoas muscle which is bunched up, thick, short, hard, and painful when worked. When a person with scoliosis lies down, the leg on the thick, hard side is shorter than the other and tends to turn out.

Moshe would push this leg toward the head making it even shorter. Now the muscle which has been pulling the leg cannot work because Moshe is pushing the leg shorter than the muscle can pull it. Since the muscle cannot work, it has to relax. Then Moshe would stretch the other psoas muscle even longer. Being thus stimulated, the muscle gets new blood which brings nourishment and removes wastes. A new awareness is created in both muscles so that when Moshe lets go, both muscles are more balanced than before.

In his group work Moshe strived to enhance awareness in action. He tried to increase a person's sensitivity to his or her body by emphasizing movements done in small gradients with complete awareness. Usually he began simply by bringing awareness into the act of lying on the floor:

Everyone examines attentively the contact of his body with the floor and gradually learns to detect considerable differences, points where the contact is feeble or non-existent and others where it is full and distinct. This training develops the awareness of the location of the muscles which produce the weak contact through the permanent, excessive tension of holding parts of the body up from the floor. A certain improvement in comportment can be achieved through muscular awareness only but beyond that no improvement will be carried over into normal life without increasing the awareness of the skeleton and its orientation. Here the most difficult joints are the hip joints. The awareness of the location and function in these joints is non-existent compared with that of people who sit on the ground and not on chairs. The chair sitter is almost without exception completely out of place when locating the hip joints. Moreover, he uses his legs as if they were articulated at the points where he has them articulated in his body image and not where they are.

I usually make it clear that the work is to lead to awareness in action, or the ability to make contact with one's own skeleton and muscles and with the environment practically simultaneously. This is not relaxation, for true relaxation can be maintained only when doing nothing. The aim . . . is healthy, powerful, easy and pleasurable exertion. The reduction of tension is necessary because efficient movement is effortless.[5]

For a wide range of human activities the Fechner-Weber law states that the least detectable difference is determined by the ratio of the change in the stimulus to the overall stimulus. Moshe said:

If I hold a twenty pound weight, I cannot detect a fly landing on it because the least detectable difference in the stimulus is half a pound. On the other hand, if I hold a feather, a fly landing on it makes a great difference. Obviously then, in order to be able to tell differences in exertion one must first reduce the exertion. Finer and finer performance is possible only if the sensitivity, that is, the ability to feel the difference is improved.[6]

Consequently, Moshe urged his clients to do less than they could. Then they could maintain full awareness in the movement and, without knowing, extend themselves beyond the limit they would have set for themselves had they begun by pushing themselves to the maximum. Slow, sometimes barely perceptible, and always unstrained movements are used to create a state of awareness in which the body can observe what works and what does not. When awareness fills a movement, a person can drop the parasitic movements and do gracefully, smoothly, and gently just the essential movement. Most movements require the activation of very few muscles, around five percent or ten at the most. This means that ninety to ninety-five percent must be inhibited. Increasing the awareness of a movement leads to activating only the right muscles and inhibiting the rest.

When awareness pervades the body, a person's self-image is complete. When a person's self-image is complete, he or she embodies gracefulness. Consider Moshe's description of the correct posture:

The erect posture is a biological quality of the human frame, and there should be no sensation of doing, holding, or any effort whatsoever. The actual posture is always the result of what the frame would do thanks to inherent mechanisms and what we have learned to do by adjusting ourselves to our physical and social environment. Much of what we have learned is to the detriment of the system, for it has been learned under the duress of affection or the stress of hardship when immediate dependence on others distorted our real needs. . . .

The dynamic conception of erect posture is as follows: The body should be so organized that it can start any movement, that is, forward, backward, right, left, down, up, turning either way, without previous arrangement of the segments of the body, without any sudden change in the rhythm of breathing, without clenching the lower jaw or tensing the tongue, and without any perceptible tensing of the muscles of the neck or fixation of the eyes. In this state the head is not fixedly held in space, but is free to move gently in all directions without previous notice. If these conditions are maintained during the action, then even lifting the entire weight of the body is not sensed as an effort.[7]

REWIRING THE NERVOUS SYSTEM

IN FELDENKRAIS work, the client's body is usually put into a passive position, either lying on a table or on the floor. Pillows and rollers are used to relieve any muscles that might still be working. Once the body is as passive as possible, small movements are made to bring into awareness normally unconscious, habitual patterns of movement or tension and to allow these patterns to fall away. The movements are light, and after fifteen or twenty repetitions the effort drops to practically nothing more than a thought. This produces maximum sensitivity in the person and enables one to detect minute changes in muscle tone and alignment of different parts of the body. As awareness increases, maladaptive patterns naturally fall away.

These patterns are tied to habitual structural and emotional patterns which are also unconscious. When the maladaptive functional pattern is broken, a person's structure, emotions, and environment also improve "whether you like it or not," as Moshe used to say. The following are cases from my Feldenkrais work.

The School Teacher's Neck

His head lay over toward his left shoulder. For seven years he had not been able to move it toward the center. I tried to move it toward center, and his whole back went into spasm. He groaned with pain.

He told me he suffered from this neck problem after a severe car accident. The x-rays and other tests showed no organic damage that would cause such restriction. He had gone from one doctor to another for years, trying to get relief, but to no avail. He contacted Moshe, but Moshe was going back to Israel so he sent this man to me.

I found that the shoulder could be lifted with no spasm and that the head could be brought to center when the shoulder was brought with it. I kept doing this movement, lifting the head and shoulder as one piece until the head was straight over the body. Then I let the neck, head and shoulder go back to the aberrated position. Slowly, I separated the shoulder movement from the neck movement until I could bring the head and shoulder up so the head was straight and then drop the shoulder while holding the head in position. There was no pain or spasm. His shoulder was down and his head was up straight.

Tears rolled down his cheeks as he looked in the mirror and sobbed, "What will I tell my wife? What will I tell my students? What will I tell my neighbors?"

The Crane Operator's Back

His back was in spasm, and it was very painful for him to be down on the floor doing the Feldenkrais lessons with 250 other people in the seminar I was leading. The pain got worse each time he moved. Later he told me that he kept saying to himself, "Thank God, Dub is here to take care of me. I know I will have to be carried out on a stretcher. I may die right on the floor."

He would go for many months, building up tension in his back as he operated his multi-story crane, and then when he could not bear the pain any longer, he would come to me and be Rolfed. It was a cycle: develop the pain, get Rolfed and lose the pain; develop the pain, get Rolfed again, and so on.

At my suggestion, he signed up for the seminar. On that fifth seminar night, he went through an hour with much pain. He did the movement in his head when it was too painful to actually move his muscles and bones. That night for the first time he got rid of the pain by himself, without either Rolfing or drugs. And I lost another good customer.

The Mystery Cure

A steel cable had snapped and whipped around Glen's right side. It had pulled him into some machinery which mangled him. Somehow they saved him, and years later a medical doctor sent him to me to see what I could do about his crippled body. I worked the

Feldenkrais Method with him and slowly got some of the spasm and pain out, but it wouldn't stay out.

One night I went to his home to see if I could relieve a very painful attack, and we stumbled onto a peculiar thing. When he turned his eyes to the right, it triggered off all the old pain and trauma of the accident, just as if the cable were once more whipping at him. Just moving his eyeballs to the right could send his whole body into a spasm.

I gave him some exercises to differentiate his eye movements from his head movements. Normally they are tied together, but in this case I had him hold his head still while he moved his eyes in all directions except the right. Then I asked him to move his eyes slightly off center to the right and back to center. Gradually we increased this distance, but I made sure he brought his eyes back to center at the first hint of triggering a spasm. In this way he gradually began to increase his freedom of movement and shrink the area which triggered his spasms. I showed him several exercises in eye movements for the same purpose.

Some months passed, and the doctor who had referred him called to tell me how much better Glen was and thanked me for my contribution. I said nothing. I was very embarrassed for I had not seen him since that night.

My mind went to work. Whom had he gone to? A chiropractor, a physical therapist, another Feldenkrais practitioner? I knew my work had shown little improvement. I rang Glen up and asked how he was. He answered, "Much better, getting better all the time." I asked if I could come down and see him.

He met me at the door. It was obvious that he was moving more easily and with much less pain. I told him how much better he looked and asked him what he was doing to get the improvement.

"I just do the exercises you gave me," he said. I had completely forgotten that I had given him a series of Awareness through Movement lessons to do on his own.

She Made Love like a Door

She said that sex with college men was no good for her and that she was experimenting at having sex with another woman. She mentioned the name of another client who was married.

I told her that as long as her pelvis was frozen she would not be able to get or give much sexual satisfaction. I told her it was like making love with an oak door as a partner. She got mad.

Well, to make a long story short it was reported to me by my married client that she got her pelvis free and working, found herself a boyfriend, and is happy with her sex life.

The married woman found a happy life with her husband and family after we finished her series.

Rolfing Through Awareness

He experienced extreme pain as I Rolfed one side of his body, and when we finished that side, neither of us wanted to continue on the other.

I told him that I would review what we had done in our work on the one side, and if he could remember and recreate in his mind all the moves, feelings, sensations, et cetera, and transfer them to the other side of his brain, he might be able to process the unworked side of his body by himself.

I reviewed all the moves I would make if I were actually doing the second side, and I asked that he remember each move and the associated pain he experienced when the first side was done. I put my hand lightly on his leg and asked if he remembered how it felt when I went deeply between the two muscles—and I asked him to reproduce the whole experience, including the pain and moaning. This he did.

I left the room after a few minutes of watching and met another Rolfer in the hall outside my office. Since we could both hear my client going through his painful, noisy re-experience and since I was not there, he asked what was going on in my room. I told the astonished Rolfer that my client was Rolfing himself.

Upon checking, I found that the results of the two sides were equally good, and in some ways the second was even better. When this story got out, I had a lot of explaining to do to Ida.

Running in Your Mind

Stewart, an *est* trainer, came in for his Rolfing session. He was complaining that Werner had a new rule that all staff had to run each week. Stewart is not known for his physical powers, nor is he known for doing anything that isn't necessary or pleasant to do. He was looking for a way out, and I gave it to him.

I said, "Put your feet up on your desk and do your running in your head." This kind of running was more to Stewart's liking.

Stewart came in some weeks later, all smiles. He had been running in his head with his feet on his desk. His colleagues caught up to him and made him run in the real world. They timed him and compared it with his first run weeks earlier and found he had cut more time off his run that those who had pounded the pavement faithfully each week. All agreed that Stewart could continue to run with his feet on his desk.

The Little Old Lady's Battered Knee

When the little eighty-year-old lady came through my door, she looked like she had been knocked down by a bus. She told me she had been knocked down by a runner as she got off the bus. We got all her torn and soiled clothes off except for her pants. I asked her if she had any pain. She said just her right knee. It was the same when she moved about—just the right knee. The right knee was bloody, gritty, and grimy.

I had her lie down and placed a roller under her knees and a pillow under her head. I decided to work her neck first, to get her calmed down and into the "here and now." After she relaxed, I left the neck and went to the good left knee. I then pressed around the imagined damaged tissue on the left knee making sure she had her awareness under my fingers.

I continually asked her if there was any pain and made sure her awareness remained with the left knee. I slowly pressed on one spot and then another until I had covered the whole knee area many times. Then I asked her if she would look and see if she had any pain anywhere. Her answer was no.

I moved the good knee slowly about, getting her awareness in every movement. She reported no pain. I then did the same thing with the damaged knee and she again reported no pain. I got my bottle of witch hazel and Kleenex and washed the blood and dirt from the injured knee.

After I worked her neck and back she got up and walked around the room with no pain. I suggested she might want to see a doctor and be checked over. In any event, she was to call the next morning.

She called the next day to report that the banged up knee felt great but the undamaged knee was a little sore, and she could not understand this.

The Ballet Star

As he tried to stand on his feet, he almost fell to the floor. He spent minutes trying to find his new balance. Finally he gave up, sat on the floor, and sobbed. He was a star ballet dancer and was scheduled to perform that evening at the university.

After he calmed down, he tried some simple ballet movements, and finally sat down at a complete loss about what to do. I had not known he had a performance that evening, or I would not have completely changed his balance. I would have balanced what was already there. Now we had to work with what we had.

I suggested he go home and spend the next three hours doing his performance in his head. We had done Feldenkrais work together before, and he felt he could do it. I told him to do it perfectly and slowly, many times, and I assured him he would be able to perform well. I got tickets and went to the performance. I wasn't sure what would happen.

The first time he came on stage he did well, but he seemed to float—almost as if he were dancing in slow motion. The second time he came on stage, and every time thereafter his performance was flawless.

I went backstage after the performance, and he was all smiles as he took compliments from the crowd that surrounded him. I finally got him alone.

He said the director caught him as he came off stage the first time, told him his movements had no snap, and asked if he was on drugs. He told the director that he had been Rolfed that day, then went off by himself backstage and did the rest of his performance in his imagination—this time with plenty of snap. After the performance, the director told him that he had just finished his finest performance.

ZEN BODYTHERAPY

DUBBING

AFTER TRAINING with Moshe I began integrating his work with Ida's. I also studied joint manipulation with Lauren Berry, trigger points with John St. John, and Trager work with Milton Trager. Eventually following the suggestion of Jack Swartz, I called my own way of working "Dubbing." I developed an elaborate theoretical model which emphasized the identity of the mind and body I have so often witnessed in my work. Figure 2 summarizes this model. While it cannot do justice to the complexity of change in the human being, it highlights the holistic nature of the process.

By body tone I mean the tonus of the soft connective tissue of the body. Of the three types of muscle tissue, I focus primarily on the skeletal muscles that move the bones. These can be divided into antagonistic pairs, the flexors and the extensors. The flexor muscles fold or bend the joint or body while the antagonistic, extensor muscles must relax and lengthen. When one partner fires and shortens, the other must relax and allow the movement to occur. Any other action aberrates the movement. When both antagonistic muscles fire the same amount at the same time, a spastic condition results. Problems occur when muscles fire heavily all the time, when they never fire enough to get good tone, or when antagonistic muscles lack balance in their tone.

Muscle quality or tone is measured by the difference in the muscle's length when it is relaxed and when it is firing. This difference determines how far that muscle can move the bone. A muscle that is either too hard or too soft will not have much differential. Ideally the muscle is resilient. It is long and pliable when not firing and shortens and hardens when firing. Such muscles have good tone. They are filled with oxygen and glucose, free of excess waste

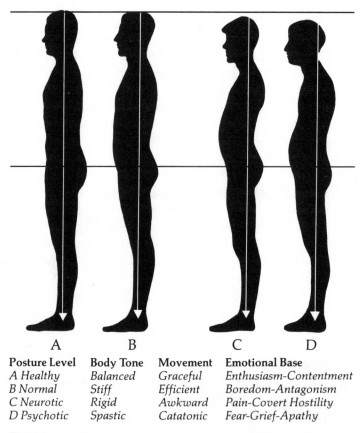

Posture Level	Body Tone	Movement	Emotional Base
A Healthy	Balanced	Graceful	Enthusiasm-Contentment
B Normal	Stiff	Efficient	Boredom-Antagonism
C Neurotic	Rigid	Awkward	Pain-Covert Hostility
D Psychotic	Spastic	Catatonic	Fear-Grief-Apathy

Figure 2.
(Based on original drawings with permission from International Universities Press, Inc.)

and acid, and clean of old traumas and scars. The opposite conditions characterize poor body tone.

By movement I mean both the internal movements of the body and the movement of the body in the external environment. The ideal is the graceful movements of the healthy person with balanced muscle tone. The norm is the relatively inefficient movement of the average person. The most restricted is the catatonic psychotic with spastic muscles.

With the emotional scale I simply suggest a range of emotions characterizing each level. The healthy person experiences happiness and sadness according to the natural rhythms of life. He has a home base near enthusiasm and contentment and will move up and down the emotional scale easily and appropriately, but will always return to a happy home base. The normal person clings to things, regrets the past, and worries about the future. His home base is in boredom and antagonism. The neurotic swings between pain and covert hostility; he is trapped in the tensions of his body and the circles of his mind. He cannot really experience life and takes an adversarial stance towards others. The psychotic is overwhelmed by life. He seeks to escape the terror of existence and find some semblance of peace in apathy.

I once saw a woman dramatically move up the scale from feelings of worthlessness to happiness. At the start of the session she moaned and complained about an endless list of failures as I worked her body. Toward the middle of the session, she moved from a sense of failure to apathy. Time was running out, and I did not want to leave her mucking around in apathy so I worked to get her angry. After some time I succeeded, and she told me how angry she was as I walked with her from my office to the stairs.

I pointed out to her that actually she had gone up the scale a long way from feeling like a total failure to feeling angry. She understood what I meant, laughed, and moved further up to cheerfulness. She gave me a peck on the cheek, thanked me, and then left.

Technically Dubbing basically consisted of: 1. Soft tissue work, 2. Joint manipulation, and 3. Nervous system reprogramming. If the soft tissue is hard, brittle, and thick, then Rolfing and trigger point work is clearly needed at some point. If a joint is out of socket, then joint manipulation may be the quickest way to relieve pain and improve functioning. If a movement is painful and the problem is not in the soft tissue or joints, then reprogramming neuromuscular patterns through the Feldenkrais methods is indicated. Often the best treatment combines all three approaches.

The first task is to relieve the body of pain. This is usually accomplished by releasing the trauma stored in trigger points through the application of pressure. Trigger points are places in the body where tensions and poisons accumulate. Janet Travell and David Simons, two physicians pioneering work in this field, define trigger points as:

A focus of hyperirritability in a tissue that, when compressed, is locally tender and, if sufficiently hypersensitive, gives rise to referred pain and tenderness, and sometimes to referred autonomic phenomena and distortion of proprioception. Types include myofascial, cutaneous, fascial, ligamentous, and priosteal trigger points.[1]

Trigger points can be in soft connective tissue and can refer pain to a trigger point in distant connective tissue. It may refer pain to an organ or an organ may refer pain to a trigger point. Both active and static pressures are used to relieve trigger points, and the variables are infinite. How much pressure and how much movement, in what direction and for how long? The bodytherapist must be able to change what he is doing in an instant according to the unique needs of the body before him.

Once the tissue is soft and relatively free of stored trauma, joints can be repositioned and the body structure realigned. But the client benefits more if he develops a functional awareness of the changes occurring as his body is worked. As his awareness of how his body lines up in the field of gravity increases, he integrates the changes into the way he habitually holds himself. The improvements generalize to the internal and external movements of his body. His whole life expands for the better; he attains a higher level of well-being.

When I work with people, I first get them to take responsibility for their own problem. If a person has pain, is out of alignment, cannot move easily, or whatever the problem is, he cannot lie back and expect to be fixed without being actively involved in the healing process himself. It is his pain, misalignment, or constriction, and his choice what to do about it. If he chooses to keep his problem, or if he wants to give up only certain symptoms, whatever he wants and chooses, I will support him. I explain to clients that they are in complete control of the work we do together. He can ask me to stop or lighten up, and I will do just that.

If painful emotions emerge during a session, I assure my clients that they can handle anything that comes up; otherwise they would not bring it up. I promise to stay in touch with them physically and to give them all my support while they relive and release their traumas. I may sometimes ask them to go over and over the traumatic incident until the emotional intensity disappears. Unless they have a need to relate their stories, I prefer not to hear them. When a client goes through a trauma, he is dramatically changed. His face and voice are soft and clear. His love for himself and others blossoms. It is a joy to serve people in this way. Below are the stories of some of the people I had the chance to work with during this period of my life.

Lauren Berry

The phone rang. It was Loretta Berry from Redding. She said Lauren was not well, wanted to sleep all the time, and was grouchy. She asked if I would come up.

That afternoon I found Lauren sleeping on the sofa. I slipped my hands under his neck and began to slowly, gently massage his disorganized neck. He stirred and looked back at me and smiled. I said, "I love you, Lauren." He just patted my hands with his, and I continued working.

After the neck work, I slipped my hands under his back and worked at softening and lengthening the large muscles there for some time. Then I had Lauren turn around so I could work the muscles on the other side of the rib cage. As the large extensor muscles relaxed and regained more normal tone, Lauren's face softened.

Since he had turned end for end, I now had his feet available for work. They, like his neck, were hard and stiff, but changed quite quickly. As I started working the bottom of the foot, I discovered some very hot reflex points in the area that corresponds to the pituitary gland in the brain. Lauren could not handle the intense pain as I pressed this area of the toes and jerked his foot away.

After I finished Lauren, I told Loretta what I had found, and we decided to call one of Lauren's medical friends, a doctor near Palo Alto. The doctor talked to both Lauren and Loretta and then instructed us to get Lauren down to a Santa Rosa hospital for a brain scan.

The next morning, after the brain scan, the doctor told Loretta that they found seven tumors in Lauren's brain. I drove Lauren and Loretta back to Redding, where Lauren died a few weeks later.

Lauren Berry was the greatest body mechanic I have ever met. He seemed able to fix any mechanical body problem. I honor Lauren, an unpolished genius and a great teacher.

The Forty-eight-Hour Pain Syndrome

His new girl friend helped him up the stairs; his back was so painful that he took minutes to sit down on my stool. His large back muscles were in spasm, and the spine was badly contorted. He said he had picked up a book two days earlier; this act had triggered the pain.

He was a therapist, and we had studied Ron Hubbard's theory that there was always a loss or an imagined loss in the forty-eight hour period prior to experiencing pain which did not correspond to any physical trauma. I chided him about forgetting this, but he said he had looked and looked and could find none. I told him to continue looking, and I went to work getting the spastic muscles to relax, little by little.

All of a sudden, his girl friend's face lit up, and she blurted out, "Hell, that was the day you received the letter notifying you that your divorce was final." The spasm slowly died away. He shook my hand, and I have not seen him since, except on TV and in the papers as he does his human potential thing.

Another Forty-eight-Hour Pain Syndrome

A Stanford teacher phoned and said she was on the floor, could not get up, and wanted an appointment right now. I told her that I could not see her until the next afternoon and asked what had happened. She said she was just picking up a pen, and her back went out. I suggested some movements that eased the pain somewhat. Then I asked her to look and see if she had had a loss or an imagined loss during the forty-eight hours prior to the start of the pain.

She could not remember any. I explained that if she could find such a loss or trauma and experience it fully, then the back would probably get better. She said she would continue looking, and we set up an appointment for the following afternoon.

The next morning she called me and happily reported her pain was gone. Her youngster had poured a box of soap in the washer. It overflowed, and the motor burned out. She canceled her appointment, and I never saw her.

Work Your Extensors, and Change Your Head

I was driving down Highway 91, and tears were running down my cheeks. My hands were squeezing the steering wheel. My body was rolled over as I cupped my hands on the wheel. Shudders brought waves of sadness emanating from every cell of my body.

I looked at what was going on and said to myself, "I don't want this! I want to die and get away from it all! Then it struck me that I did not have to die to get change. I remembered that the extensor muscles of the body can change your level of being. If the flexors relax and lengthen, as the extensors gain tone and straighten the body and its appendages, then my thoughts would be more positive and I would feel better.

Well, I lengthened and straightened my spine, got my head up toward the top of the car, straightened and lengthened my arms, legs and fingers, and visualized getting longer, taller and softer. Thirty miles down the road, I was whistling and tapping my foot to my own music.

The Drooping Right Side

She said the medical profession could not put a name to her problem. They said it was not multiple sclerosis or a stroke. Another practitioner brought her in. He did not know what to do and neither did I. Her right side was weaker and shorter than her left. Even her right eye drooped somewhat. Her condition had been developing for a couple of years and was deteriorating more each month.

I worked her neck to get us both into the here and now and to establish trust. Then I put my right hand over her navel. The area from the ribs to the pelvis was unusually hard. I worked the superficial soft tissue in the area, and as it relaxed and lengthened I went deeper. For two hours, my hands worked this area, finding ropes, belts, sheaths that disappeared as I gently worked them.

Finally, I got down to the iliopsoas muscle in the pelvic area, and here I found the right muscle to be somewhat tighter and more stringy than the left. After working the right side, I asked the lady to take a walk and see what was going on. She walked to the far side of the room and, as she came back, she said, "Now the right side is stronger and better than the left."

I couldn't believe my eyes. Her symptoms were gone. Even her droopy right eye no longer drooped.

The Hammer Toes

A woman had very severe hammer toes on her left foot only and could not take either the Rolfing or Feldenkrais method of working the toes. These manipulations worked fine on her right toes. We ended up with one set of hammer toes and one set of soft, long flexible toes. Since she had been trained in using the "E" meter to clear trauma, I suggested we try this.

The "E" meter measures people's responses to emotionally "charged" subjects. By monitoring how well the body conducts electricity, it shows when a person is avoiding any uncomfortable or painful thought or feeling.

After we worked awhile, she re-experienced the pain of standing on her left toes in ballet school. She cried, carried on, and finally let go of that incident. Then an earlier incident with her mother emerged, and then one with her father. Her crying really peaked then. All the while I watched the meter and softly worked her toes as Moshe had done mine.

After she finished processing the incident with her father and dried her tears, she found she had two sets of matching, long, flat, soft toes. Neither of us could believe what we saw.

Clearing Myself with the "E" Meter

"The meter shows I'm not confronting the incident," I thought.

As the thought went through my mind, the facilitator asked, "What was that? When did it happen? How long did the incident last? Go to the beginning and scan through that incident from beginning to end, and then tell me what happened."

"I was in the third grade," I said, "and it was at recess. We were playing basketball. I jumped up to catch the ball, and someone hit my feet. I fell down and hit the back of my head on the concrete. I could not get up for a few minutes. When I went back to the classroom, I felt very dizzy and sick.

"The teacher asked me to read aloud to the class. The printed words ran together, shifted, and were generally blurred. I made a mess of reading, and the teacher told me that I did poorly. I dropped my head and began to cry. The wooden floor boards were moving in waves and shifting back and forth. I got sick to my stomach. The teacher got my brother, and he took me home."

After I recounted this story, I told the facilitator that I could never read aloud. The print would blur and shift, and I would stumble over the simplest words. This made me feel stupid. He asked me to close my eyes, scan through the incident again, and tell him if I found anything new. We did this repeatedly, until I began laughing on the fifth scan.

The facilitator asked what happened, and I told him that while I was lying on my back on the concrete, half-unconscious, I kept struggling to get up to beat the hell out of my cousin, who had knocked me down. I couldn't move, though, and I was very angry at my cousin but even angrier at myself for not being able to work him over.

Through all these years I had blamed the teacher for traumatizing me when I was really angry at myself. This unresolved anger put me right back in the third grade with words swimming before my eyes every time I tried to read aloud. Realizing the truth freed my eyes and brain from the old, dysfunctional pattern.

Choosing To Stay Stuck

Almost weekly someone with a body problem says he wants help and has been unable to find help anywhere. Such people will not take responsibility for getting rid of their problem and will strongly deny that they are getting a lot of goodies from having their problem. With a client like this, the practitioner is beaten before he starts. Nothing will work until the client's attitudes and desires are turned around.

I recall a young man who came in, using a cane and in deep back pain. He could move only with great distress. I took his shirt off and had him sit on a stool, since it looked like a major project to have him lie down. When I started, he could hardly stand me touching his back where he had scars from two operations. When I finished, I could put steady pressure on these areas without his complaining of pain. It was also clear to me that he moved much more easily and freely than when he came in.

When I asked him if he could see any changes, he said, "No, it is just the same as before I was operated on the first time."

He told me that he was getting insurance checks, had a little hobby going that he enjoyed, and was waited on by his family. He also said that he did not like the heavy work he was doing when he fell and hurt his back. It was clear to me that he was happier with his pain and hobby than with his hard job and healthy body.

Ending the Child Abuse Cycle

She had had ten sessions of Rolfing, but her back still bothered her in the same way. She was disappointed, and I felt like a failure. When she had called a few days before, I had told her to come back, and I would do whatever necessary to get the pain out and the mobility in, at no cost to her.

As I was about to finish working her back, she went into a crying jag. Her father used to beat her across the back. Her mother could do nothing but watch and scream. Her father beat her just as he had been beaten in his youth.

When the crying stopped, a new, fresh, relaxed person emerged. She told me that the night before she had babysat for a friend, and when the baby cried she had wanted to beat him. She had wanted to kill that baby. She said she wanted children, but knew that she could not have any as long as her head was screwed on that way. Now she felt she could care for children without being compelled to work out her own trauma on them.

Dubbing Goes to College

The names of twelve students were randomly chosen to participate in this experiment. The students were given ten sessions of one-on-one body work and my brand of awareness and movement exercises for twenty group classes.

All participants took the FIRO-B and FIRO-F tests before and after, and all kept diaries of their feelings and body changes. The FIRO-B and FIRO-F tests were developed by Will Schutz, author of *Here Comes Everybody, The Interpersonal Underworld*, and a number of other books. These tests measure a person's ability and desire to communicate and participate with others.

Afterwards Schultz analyzed the data. In summary this is what he wrote:

The group of 12 started as people with low desire for human contact (inclusion) and intimacy (affection), and a strong desire—strongest ever measured for a group—to be told what to do (want control).

The group ended in a moderated position in all of these areas. They went up on a wanting inclusion and wanting affection and expressing affection, and they went down on wanting to be controlled. All changes were not only consistent and significant, but were very large. Their desire to be thought competent by other people also dropped significantly.

The picture is one of people who became willing to control their own lives and who had an increased desire to interact with people both socially and with intimacy.

Well done, Dub.

What follows are the accounts of two students in this group.

E's Seventh Session

"My seventh hour was incredible. It was literally like having my entire life flash before my eyes on a movie screen. I remember several things which relate very heavily to my sexuality and my dealings with my father. Since that hour I have begun to feel more at ease with my father and enjoy being with him much more. I've let go of a lot of things I didn't realize I was holding against him. I have also had my head turned around or perhaps straightened out about my sexuality. I no longer feel stuck into being gay but rather that it is a choice. I feel I understand a lot more about why I've chosen to be gay. I don't know if I will remain exclusively gay or go very straight, or have a combination or what. I do know, however , that whichever sex I choose to have a relationship with it will be for reasons beyond sex and if it's a man, it's a man or if it's a woman, it's a woman. I guess I've learned that you can't receive much without being open, not just open with your body sexually, but with your soul, your heart, your feelings, who you are. I used to think I was open, but what I really was, was vulnerable. I'm learning to be open. Sometimes it hurts and sometimes it's lovely as hell—but it's a start towards something better, I can tell that much. I'd like to share with you what I wrote in my diary the night I got home from this session.

Vision 1

"I am eight years old. My best friend Ron and I are playing. I put on my sister's petticoat. I fasten it around my waist. It's like a long skirt, it is pink and frilly. I put it on to play and go across the street. My father comes home from work. He is embarrassed, ashamed, angry. He grabs me around the arm and shoulder and drags me home through the back gate to the garbage can, rips it off me and throws it in the garbage can so I'll never be able to play with it again. I'm sorry, I cry and beg him not to throw it away. I had fun playing, pretending. I didn't understand why he was so angry. What had I done that was such a bad thing? I see now that he was probably tired, frustrated. We were very poor, and he worked very hard. He used to come home and scoop me up in his arms and call me 'sun-shine.' I was his son-shine. I loved him so much. I'm crying right now. I'm sorry I held it against you all these years. I'll try to let go. I am a man, daddy. He loves me, I know that. I'm sorry, I'm sorry—I say I'm sorry during the session. Dub misunderstands. I'm not talking to him, I'm talking to my father.

Vision 2

"Dub is working with his finger in my mouth. I feel like I'm going to gag. Dub stops, he starts again, I look up. His finger is not a finger but a penis going into my mouth. I want to close my eyes but I keep them open. Part of me keeps saying, 'What don't you want to see?' I feel scared, frightened, excited. I remember my first homosexual experience. I am a senior in high school. It is the day before my senior portrait is taken. I go to a dirty men's bathroom in this discount department store in my town. I sit in a stall, someone sits in the stall next to me.

I leave my stall and enter his. He sits there playing with himself, an unattractive red-faced man. He sucks me off. I almost can't come. I shake like a leaf. He tries to be nice and asks me if it was my first time. I say, 'Yes,' very quietly.

He smiles and says, 'Don't worry, it gets easier.' I leave immediately and sit in my car thinking never, never again—but I know, I know then it will happen again and again."

N's Eighth Session

"After the session I stood up, and Dub asked me how I felt. Through tears I said, 'I'm in the middle of a cloud.'

'Lie back down,' he said and gently worked on my neck. At some point, he went out for a few moments; then I was vaguely aware of Dub's coming in, of his touch. I was aware of his love for me, and my love for him.

"Then after some time, very clearly and suddenly I saw a two-inch square of brown floor. Saw the grain of the wood, a place where the wood had splintered and was ripped out, and then as I scanned, saw the entire floor and knew where I was: in the living room of the barn-red house. I saw my father's brown upholstered Morris chair, a tan suitcase, an arm (my daddy's) throwing clothes into the suitcase atop each other. And I saw myself, age ten and a half, taking them out, one by one, as he threw them in, folding each one carefully. I needed to cry out, but I carefully folded clothes.

"Now I was in the kitchen. I felt my fear of my father leaving forever. The room filled with the terror of this. The white counter in the kitchen at the parsonage where we had lived, the blue-green kitchen table and the woodstove, all came back with the feeling this room had. This day, December 10, 1953, didn't come from nowhere; it had been building at least since my grandmother's arrival, in August. The terribly strained, painful feeling in that kitchen. Day after day of strain, tension, mistrust, my mother's silent oppression, fragments of conversation leaving everything that needed to be said between them, unspoken.

"Before I lost consciousness, Dub came back in, and put his hand over my navel, very firmly, until I came out of it and back into the present, into the room. Then, after some time passed and it was over, I felt very light, cleansed, and tired and became aware of a horrible stench in the room."

Alvin

The phone rang. It was Alvin's son. He said his father was in the hospital with a heart attack and that he had asked for me. My friend Audrey was with me and drove me down.

As I sat in the car, I was wondering if my three-hour workshop the day before could have been a contributing factor to Alvin's heart attack. He had contacted the producer of the workshop, told her about his hypertension problem, and asked if my workshop would resolve the problem. When the question was referred to me, I said I did not see how the workshop could cause him a problem and that it should be beneficial.

Alvin was an attorney, which caused me to give second thought to my decision. I had just lost a ten-year real estate lawsuit to an attorney which cost me over $200,000. Audrey, who was also in the workshop, tried to assure me that I was not to blame.

I told Audrey that I could not understand why Alvin wanted to see me. I had just met him. Yet, without really having time to get to know him, I felt great affinity for him. But if I was not at fault, why should he call for me? Audrey said that Alvin just wanted to see and experience me again. I could not see this at all. We had only spent three hours together with twenty other people.

I remembered how I had prepared for this workshop, how I had reviewed many Awareness through Movement lessons and chosen three. Then, after I had spent so much time choosing the lessons, I had realized that the lessons were not the important thing to teach. The important thing was the process, Moshe's learning how to learn process. After considerable re-reading and review, I felt prepared to teach the process. Then I realized that neither the lessons nor the process were what made a good workshop. The important thing was who I was and letting who I was hang out and be shared with everyone so that they could feel, see, and enjoy who they really were. That was what I wanted to do. With this thought, I put all my books and papers away and went out and sat by the ocean and meditated. I left the ocean and went directly to the workshop.

Now, a day later, as we drove toward the hospital, I planned what I would do when I got there. I would touch Alvin's head with my right hand, let him know I loved him, and tell him that he would be all right.

Alvin's wife met us in the hall and said the doctor did not want any visitors and asked for my thoughts. I told her that whatever was best for Alvin was the only thing I wanted. She left and returned in a few minutes saying Alvin wanted to see me.

He was lying there with tubes in his nose and chest and opened his eyes as I came closer. I put my left hand on his head and, as I did so, I said to myself, "Ida would say it should be your right hand, and I can't reach across with my right hand. I'll just make it work to use my left hand."

As I touched his forehead, I felt my face change and tears came to my eyes. I said, "I love you."

Alvin replied, "Yes, I know." His voice was stronger than mine.

The room filled with love, and I said, "I'm leaving, but I will be with you, and I love you." I left with tears running down my cheeks and waited in the hall close to the wall for a few moments while I collected myself and then went and joined Audrey.

Alvin's son came running down the hallway, thanked me for coming, and said my visit had done something for his father. I told the son that it was indeed an honor and privilege for Alvin to ask me to come, and I thanked him. There were tears in his eyes too.

Audrey and I drove to the beach where we walked and talked. It was clear to Audrey that Alvin, after being in the seminar, had contacted the love he had for himself. He also felt this love in me. It took me a long time that night to understand all this.

Finally, Audrey's message got through: "Dub, you always are the last one to see the love and beingness you have." I guess that is the way it is for each of us.

TANOUYE TENSHIN ROSHI

ALVIN brought me to Chozen-ji, the International Zen Dojo in Hawaii, to meet Tanouye Tenshin, the Zen master there. As I walked onto the grounds of the temple in Kalihi Valley, I felt a calm serenity. At my first meeting with Tanouye Roshi, his shining eyes, his ready sense of humor, his quickness, vitality, and openness impressed me. He wore blue coveralls and looked more like a laborer than a Zen master, but there was a relaxed concentration about him that made me self-conscious.

We sat in the dining area talking freely. At one point he asked me about my work. I told him a little about Ida Rolf and Moshe Feldenkrais and their work. I mentioned that Ida had been active in Yoga and that Moshe had been Judo champion of Britain and had written two books on the subject. At one point I asked if I could come to rest my tired body for two weeks. He did not answer and seemed to have no interest in my staying. Very disappointed, I gave up the idea.

As I shook hands with him on leaving, he surprised me by inviting me to come and stay for two weeks. I asked when I should come. He answered, "Come as soon as you can as long as I'm around to teach you." To be trained in Zen—I didn't know about that. Little did I realize that he was a master body therapist who was to be my new teacher.

When I came back, after watching me work, Tanouye Roshi said he liked my system of massage but would teach me to do the same things more quickly and easily. He said he would teach me how to use energy. I pondered his statement. In the late sixties and early seventies I had poohpoohed the healers that I met at Esalen. Their claim to use esoteric energies seemed to be an excuse for a

Tanouye Roshi in his Kendo armor

lack of power to do deep tissue work. Was Tanouye Roshi any different? Certainly there was no questioning the strength that radiated from him.

We were working on a lady whose wrist was very aberrated. The muscles of the arm were holding the bones out of alignment. I told him what I saw, and he suggested I fix it. I knew I could get the two bones of the forearm separated and freed from each other and then could organize the bones and muscles of the wrist joint. I figured it would take me about thirty minutes. But instead of going to work, I turned to Tanouye Roshi and asked him to fix the aberration. He looked at me in disgust and with a few strokes and a couple of quick, gentle tugs, he was finished. He handed the wrist to me to inspect. It was free and aligned. The whole process had taken about ten seconds, and the job was first rate.

Moshe and Ida knew things they did not teach, such as ways of putting nerves back into their grooves in the hard or soft tissue, using the feet to make various manipulations of the joints, facilitating the flow of life energy, and so on. These techniques have been used in the East for hundreds of years. I realized this when I returned for the two weeks and was astounded by what Tanouye Roshi saw and did with the clients we worked. I asked him if he would teach me to do the same. He said to come back for twenty-one days.

At the start of my twenty-one days of intensive training, I was very apprehensive. I was not sure what I was getting into. I had heard stories that twenty-one day trainees were required to go for days without sleep and so on. I knew I wanted to get through the training regardless. I said I was going to make it even if it killed me.

But there was another thing I knew—I did not want to sit crosslegged and meditate in zazen. I knew my legs could not stand this. I told myself and others that I would return to San Francisco on the next plane if I was forced to sit. So I asked Tanouye Roshi right off, "Do I have to sit?" I explained that sitting in the crosslegged position was not good for the Western physical structure. I explained that the Japanese knee joint was so much thicker and their legs so much shorter, that they, therefore, were better able to handle the stresses of sitting cross-legged. Moreover, I said that the Japanese knew where their hip joints really were—in the front towards the midline of the body, while Westerners thought they were on the outside of the hip on the top of the greater trochanter, inches away from the ball and socket.

Tanouye Roshi did not seem to be upset or displeased in any way and just said, "No, not unless you want to." But he also told me that Bodhidharma, the founder of Zen, was a red-bearded, blue-eyed Caucasian.

When it came time to sit, who went in with the others—me! I did everything wrong. I suffered, suffered, suffered, and came out numb. It was terrible.

After the sitting, I was led to the baths, shown how to scrub down and rinse, and then soak in a small deep tub of hot, hot water. It felt wonderful. I finally got out and was led to bed. I woke up very refreshed after a seven-hour sleep.

From that day on, I have sat zazen for a half hour each morning whenever I am at the Dojo and sitting is held. I still can't understand how it all happened.

When I first sat, thoughts of pain filled my mind. I kept thinking, "How much longer must I endure this pain? What can I do to lessen the pain and shorten the time?" As the weeks went on, I noticed my breathing was deeper, not only when sitting, but deeper and freer in general. I had greater capacity when walking up hills or doing strenuous work. I also noticed my posture was improving.

Still a few weeks later, after an extremely painful sitting, I finally got to my feet, slowly limped to the door, and stepped outside. I stopped, remembering that I had not turned and bowed when I left the hall. Filled with frustration, anger, pain, and confusion, I turned to face the screen at the front upon which Bodhidharma's portrait is painted. I looked directly in his eyes and said quite audibly, "I bow to the Buddha in me, you son of a bitch!"

Actually it turned out to be thirty-one days that I stayed at the temple. During this time I was taught and shown that the universe was nothing but fields of energy constantly changing and interpenetrating without obstruction.

One night Tanouye Roshi took me out to sit with him on the porch. We talked about the magic that could be done with the use of energy. The wind was blowing hard. Trees and bushes were moving wildly; leaves and bits of debris were blowing about. I commented on the strong wind. Tanouye Roshi asked me to watch and see what happened. He made a quick movement with his hand and asked if I saw anything. I said, "No. The wind is still blowing. Everything's the same." He asked me to look around myself. Then I realized that there was no wind in an eight-to-ten-foot area around us. The leaves on the ground in front of us were still. A few feet farther out, they were bouncing about. I said, "You put an energy barrier around us." He laughed.

Then he cupped his right hand and asked me if I saw anything in it. I didn't. He gave the hand a quick movement as if to throw something to me. I felt my head being knocked back as though hit by some soft yet forceful object. It was some minutes before my head returned to normal. He said he had tossed me some energy.

Then he left the porch, walked to a hill about twenty-five feet away, and stood facing me. He asked me if I could see him. I said, "Yes, clearly."

Then he said, "What do you see now?"

"I see your feet, arms, and head but no body."

He asked, "What about now?"

I said, "I see only your head." He asked me what I saw again, and I told him I saw him as clearly as before.

He came back to the porch, and we sat for a few minutes in silence. Then he asked me what color the kitchen wall was. I told him it was an off-white. He asked me to look again. It seemed yellow. Then it was blue. He told me to look again. I said I could not see the wall because of some fog or steam or something. He said he had put some energy between me and the wall. He smiled and said, "This gives me the runs." Then he left for the bathroom.

On another occasion I learned about energy by working on Tanouye Roshi's body. I asked him what I should work on, and he said the neck or maybe the feet. I started working on the neck. It had some tightness along each side. I went to the occipital ridge and pushed in towards the top of the head. It is always painful here, but Tanouye Roshi showed no signs of pain of discomfort.

Then he said, "Hold it right there. It goes to my eye, my bad eye. It's changing, getting better . . . there, it's gone."

I released my pressure. He held his pointer finger out in front of his nose and after a moment said, "It's better, much better." We worked this area for some time, and then he checked both eyes again. He exclaimed, "It's better than the good eye!" He seemed excited and happy and said that was enough for today.

But later in the afternoon, when I thought my work for the day was finished, the Master asked, "Do you want to work another body?"

I said, "Yes, who?"

He smiled and said, "Me!"

I went to work on his feet with his knees bent. But the effect was local and did not spread. The Master then asked me to work the top of the feet with his legs extended straight out. This is the same position used to feed vital energy into the body. I put one of my knees at the bottom of his right foot and then pressed my fingers between the bones on the top of the foot. He said, "Right there. Hold it right there. It goes to my hip, to my pelvis, now to the lower back. It's letting loose, now my neck, now my ear, now my eye. My eye is changing again."

Then we worked on the left foot, and he reported, "It's going to my pelvis, now my back. It's going to my heart; it's changing! Go get Audrey and the stethoscope."

The Master said, "Hold the bottom of my feet and send your *ki* (vital energy) through the body. Let's see what happens. Yes, that's ten times stronger. Put the pressure on my left big toe. That's directly connected to my heart."

Audrey listened to his heartbeat for a few moments and then said, "It's slower and clearer now." The Master then asked her to place the stethoscope over the part of his heart that had been damaged by a heart attack a few years ago.

I continued sending energy through his feet, concentrating on the left big toe. Audrey listened. Again she reported improvement, but the sound was not sharp and clear as before. As I continued to hold the feet, we talked for a few minutes. Audrey then said that the distortion had just about disappeared.

Tanouye Roshi then said, "Audrey, move down to the lungs. I feel it there." Again Audrey reported an improvement in the clarity of the sound. The Master then said, "Now it's in the back muscles. They are softening; the strings are going. Dub, come feel." I did and felt the changes.

When I stopped working on him, Tanouye Roshi sat up and said that he felt better than he had for seven years. We seemed to have reversed the process of aging and deterioration!

We were an excited and happy threesome as we talked for some minutes, going over what had happened and how we thought it had happened. I wanted to know how much I did, and how much the Zen Master did. He said he reduced his vibrations to my level and then let my *ki* enter his feet and flow with his body. He did a number of exercises circulating the *ki* in circles through his midsection and elsewhere. He said that the warmth he felt came into his body through my hands. We discussed how I could use what we had learned to work with my clients. We knew I would have to experiment. We felt that the first thing to do was to find the best ways to open up the channels so a client's body could accept my *ki*. The Master suggested that I work between the bones of the hands and feet as I did his. Then once a person showed drowsiness, I should feed *ki* through the feet.

I asked the Master if he thought my *ki* was increasing. He said it was, so I asked him what I was doing to get this improvement. The Master said, "Aren't your hands warm after you sit *zazen*?"

I said, "Very hot." I had my answer!

After my stay was over, I returned to the Mainland and happened to meet old friends I had shared groups with at Esalen Institute many years ago. I noticed that they had not fundamentally changed much. They were older and more mature, but they were still talking about all the different things they had tried, how they were going to get themselves together by going to this seminar or that group, and then really help others. I was struck by how much deeper and grounded the men working at Chozen-ji seemed. They were serving others as their practice and had a level of training which to my knowledge cannot be matched anywhere else. So in the spring of 1985, I came back to Hawaii to stay.

Under Tanouye Roshi's supervision I have been developing a method called Zen Bodytherapy which integrates my training and experiences with Ida, Moshe, and others with the Eastern "meta-

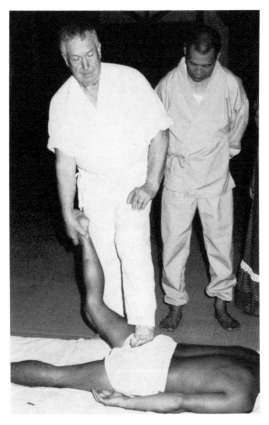

The author demonstrating Zen Bodytherapy to Hosokawa Roshi

physiology" of vital energy. I wondered about the feasibility of training others. Tanouye Roshi told me, "You know how long it took you to get to where you were when you came to me. I never trained anyone before because no one ever came to me with the amount of training you had. It would have taken me years, but bring me the right people. Have them live at the temple twenty-four hours a day for twenty-one days, and I will train them."

VITAL ENERGY

AFTER my training in structure by Ida Rolf and in function by Moshe Feldenkrais, the work with Tanouye Roshi at Chozen-ji was like a post-graduate course in reality and the meaning of life and death. It now seems clear that energy is all there is, and we are truly one with whatever is. Mike Sayama writes:

> From galaxies to atoms, from bodies to thoughts, all things are energy fields of varying degrees of permanence, power and clarity. There is a formless, cosmic sentient energy which has been called different names throughout history and across cultures, for examples: *shakti, chi, ki, mana,* and spirit. This vital energy is the subtlest manifestation of the Way.[1]

This vital energy is the essence of life. It can be sensed, but it is not explicit. Tanouye Roshi said, "You can say that the ultimate end in Zen training is to become *ki.* Then you know what T'ai Chi (The Supreme Ultimatelessness) is, what Mu (the Void) is." The structure and function of the body are also nothing but energy. To become *ki* is to experience the free flow of energy in the body and between the body and the universe. This is the experience of one's original Nature and the ultimate experience of wellness.

Aberrations in the body tissue and neuromuscular functioning are aberrations in the flow of energy. They are energy frozen in antiquated, maladaptive patterns of varying degrees of rigidity. Adding energy to the body, whether through physical pressure on tight, connective tissue or focusing attention on subtle neuromuscular functioning, releases the body from these maladaptive patterns. Increasing the energy of the body allows it to move from a condition of relative randomness to one of greater integration. Neither the structure, function, nor energy of the body can be changed without changing the others. All three are interpenetrating and need to be brought to the same level of alignment and balance. At the highest level of integration the body becomes one with the universe.

Tao

I use the term metaphysiology to refer to an understanding of human being which transcends the mind-body and organism-environment dichotomies with the notion of vital energy. Metaphysiology requires acquiring new holistic categories such as Tao, *hara*, and *kan*.

Tao or Way in Chinese philosophy is the absolute reality that cannot be named. It is not finite and cannot even be called infinite. In its essential nature it is void and ineffable. Our experience of it, however, may be most usefully expressed in terms of a universal vital energy. For example, Kaneko Shoseki described his experience of healing as follows:

> By *keiraku* I mean those imperceptible fine passages in the body which connect bones, muscles, brain, intestines, the senses, etc. with each other and eventually reconnect them all with the primal Life Force. . . . They are so to speak a network of passages which transmits to all parts of the body the spiritual-physical rhythm of the Life Force . . . .
>
> Practice every day, let go all of your fixed notions and feelings, indeed let go completely your present I. When through long serious practice you shed all preconceptions, become inwardly clear and empty you will gradually be able to delay exhalation for quite a long while and to retain the breath in the lower belly quietly. When this happens the strain of wrong effort will gradually ease, inner perception will grow clearer and in the tanden (the spiritual center in the lower abdomen) you will feel a new source of strength never before experienced—the Original Source.
>
> Apart from the normal communication between men through language and action there is another quite different sort of mutual influence. It is that of the rhythm of the Original strength which permeates all human beings and all Nature. Through it every individual in essence and, as it were, underground is connected with every other. If then one who is further removed from the working of the Primordial Force is close

91

to one who lives more in accord with it, the rhythm of the Primordial Force will certainly be transmitted from the one to the other.[2]

The great Zen master Hakuin Ekaku describes self-realization in metaphysiological terms also. He wrote:

If you distill it (vital energy) over the years, protect it to the utmost, and nourish it constantly, then before you know it the elixir-oven (the lower abdomen) and the whole universe becomes a mass of this great circulating elixir. Then you will awaken to the fact that you yourself are a divine sage with true immortality, one who was not born before heaven and earth was formed and who will not die after empty space has vanished.[3]

Hara

Hara refers to the lower back, lower abdomen, buttocks, and hips working as a unit. All movements and power in the Japanese martial arts originate from the *hara*. Basically *hara* development consists of correct breathing and posture; guidelines for both and their relation to the *hara* are given in the last chapter in the instructions for zazen. When the upper body relaxes and the strength sinks into the *hara*, vital energy radiates throughout. Energy rises up the spine, and the head feels as though it floats freely.

Hara, however, is the spiritual as well as the physical center of human being. In Japanese a matured person is described literally as "one who has made the *hara*"; and a petty, easily excitable person as "one who has not made the *hara*." Jackson Morisawa, the Kyudo (archery) instructor at Chozen-ji, writes:

Hara is the seat of life, the center of intrinsic energy. . . . It is also referred to as a state of mind in the development of one's character. One who controls the *hara* is not likely to lose his balance or composure. . . . One who has *hara* does not consume himself or spend himself completely. He learns to anchor himself in the *hara* and can shake off disturbances of the body and mind and ultimately release himself from the ego and return to the deeper power of the "original being." . . . the will is silent, the heart is quiet; and one accomplishes his work naturally without effort.[4]

Whatever the field of activity, the person who develops *hara* can transmit vitality to others much more powerfully than one who does not. In bodywork I experienced this myself recently at the Esalen Institute where I was co-leading a seminar on Zen and bodywork.

I had a cold. Several important people in my life were critically ill, and I had been doing my best to comfort them. Three days before our seminar, a boulder fell and killed Dick Price who ran Esalen and was a close friend of mine. Two hours before our seminar, I was exhausted and depressed.

Two of my co-leaders worked me. They worked their elbows into my tight back and legs. Their pressure was strong, but the pain felt good. I kept saying to myself, "Let go and let God." It was laughable; I couldn't even define god. Despite my mood, something worked as I slowly let go of the strain and trauma that I had buried in my soft tissue. I almost dozed off. Then they turned me on my back. One worked my neck; the other worked my shins and feet, and then just sent energy through my feet. I was just vaguely aware that I was being worked. Then it seemed I was alone, and my body was shuddering. Later I was told that I snored, and my body convulsed off the bed several times. Finally the shuddering stopped. I rolled over, sat up, and felt refreshed. My depression lifted, and my zest returned completely in the following days.

Neither of these men were professional masseurs, and their technique was quite crude. Yet the results they produced were of the highest level I have ever experienced. Both had developed their *hara* through long years of Zen and martial arts training. This enabled them to create and work with vital energy stronger than any I have felt apart from that of Tanouye Roshi.

Kan

Kan is transcendent intuition. It is a spontaneous, creative act which is not mediated by rational processes. It can transform any field of activity into art, but only after the forms of the field have been diligently learned. Sayama writes:

In Japanese culture the creative process is described in terms of *ki, kan,* and *myo* (wondrous action). Tanouye Roshi once thought of opening a school of fencing with the motto,"Ki ga kan o araeba, myo no oto ga

deru." (When energy strikes intuition, a wondrous sound emerges.)
When energy is intense and clear enough, transcendent intuition works,
and wondrous action emerges.[5]

In the field of bodytherapy *kan* can be described as an inner perception of patterns of energy and their interrelation between the musculature and connective tissue of the body. This perception is both a visual seeing and visceral feeling. Let me illustrate.

I was working on Brian, a big man who had been struggling with cancer for some time. He had come in bent over and limping from pain. With difficulty he got his clothes off and lay down. As I worked his neck, I asked him where he hurt. "Both front and back," he replied, putting his hands on his operation-scarred belly. For some time I worked the neck, back, feet, and lower legs. Some temporary relief from the pain came as I worked here and there, but nothing that would keep the pain from returning.

Tanouye Roshi had been in and out, watching our work and giving suggestions here and there. This time when he came in, I did not know what else I could do. He suggested I stand on a chair and look down at the body. He then asked if I saw anything unusual around the right knee. I said the color became darker around the knee. He suggested I work this area.

I sank my fingers into the tissue about two to four inches above the kneecap. I used my left had to push the right fingers deeper into the tissue. After a few seconds, my client shouted, "That's it! Hold it right there. That's it! The pain at both front and back is going. Go a little forward." I moved slightly forward without releasing the pressure. "Now move a little back." I followed his instructions until my fingers gave out. When I pulled my blue and aching hand back, he rolled off the table and moved quickly around the room shadow-boxing like a fighter. He kept saying how good he felt and how easily he could move.

None of us could believe the changes we saw. This was after a few minutes of work in the right place. Tanouye Roshi said what had happened was not explainable except as an art form.

Self-Development

I believe the field of bodywork is coming of age and now deserves acknowledgement as bodytherapy. There are many techniques to change old, dried, hard, glued tissue into soft, resilient, free tissue; to balance and align structure; to replace old, inefficient patterns of movement with graceful, desirable ones; to get constricted, painful, frozen joints working smoothly again; and much more. There is also a growing body of medical literature which substantiates this work scientifically. *The Trigger Point Manual* by Janet Travell, M.D. and David Simons, M.D., does this impressively. While bodytherapy must never compromise academic and technical training, the central importance of vital energy must be recognized. This recognition will lead to the realization that self-development and the cultivation of vital energy are inseparable.

Self-development demands rigorous mind-body training which few can complete. But for those who can make an enduring commitment to mastery, I believe that bodytherapy will become a way to the highest levels of self-development and fulfillment. It will be the challenge and pleasure of a lifetime.

CIRCULATING ENERGY

THE WELL-PROCESSED bodies turned out by Rolfing, Feldenkrais, and Zen Bodytherapy are quite different. Ida's processed bodies have a lift, a lightness that reminds me of a bullfighter. Moshe's processed bodies have more mobility and appear fluid in almost all configurations. Zen processed bodies are grounded. They seem almost unmovable by any outside force, yet they have a smooth gliding motion and never seem to lose their groundedness with the universe. All of the above well-processed bodies house psyches that are much more emotionally mature and optimistic than the non-processed. They live mostly in enthusiasm, cheerfulness, interest and contentment. When appropriate, they can move down to anger, fear and grief. Only rarely, under unusual conditions, will they drop down to despair, resentment, self-abasement or apathy. When they do, they bounce back fast. They do not "muck around" in any of the negative emotions.

Because it aims at transcending duality and becoming one with all that is, Zen Bodytherapy includes one more dimension: preparing the body for its inevitable death. This process involves reaching into the person's unconscious to allow the release of emotional as well as physical traumas which impede a smooth transition of the vital energy into the hereafter. The psychophysical cleansing of Zen Bodytherapy facilitates the natural release of vital energy at the point of death and enables a person to live fully to the last.

Below are some of my experiences of training at Chozen-ji and working with clients from a new perspective.

Fighting with Zazen

I started the zazen session by counting 1001, 1002, 1003, and so on. I then remembered that was not the way I had been instructed, but I thought, "Who are they to tell me what is best for me? Maybe there will be less pain this way. No son of a bitch is going to tell me what to do!" Then I thought back to the time Ida and three helpers dug the comment, "No son of a bitch can tell me what to do," from my solar plexus and how Ida laughed gleefully and said, "Dub, that is your ground of being."

I got back to my sitting and focused my eyes on a spot about five feet in front. The thought came to me that all there was was me. Everything else was an agreement, somebody else's agreement. Everyone agreed that beginning at my age I should have great pain in my legs when I sat zazen. Who are they to tell me what I should experience? I thought back to how coming from this ground of being had cost me a fortune. I had hired the best consultant in the furniture business to give me his recommendations. I didn't like them, so I hired who I thought was the next best, and he told me to do the same thing. I did the opposite, and it cost me a great deal of money. I also remembered losing out when two successful businessmen told me to buy the property adjoining mine, and I said to my wife, "I'm not going to let those two birds tell me what to do."

Now I thought that maybe all along I had been preparing for this part of my life. Maybe I could see what I chose, and others could do the same. If the two did not dovetail, what the hell. There is nothing there anyway. Why not have no pain in my body? As I thought this, I became aware of pain for the first time in a long while. I said to myself, "See, you create your own goddamn pain." If I choose not to have pain, let them keep their agreement and I will keep mine.

I noticed my breathing now. It was very loud; I could get some agreement on that. Surprisingly, no one yelled at me to keep quiet yet. My breathing was too rough and too high. It was in my throat and not my belly. I tried to get it down, but it stayed under my tongue in the roof of my mouth. Today I was stuck in my head.

I felt the meditation time was almost up, and a glance at the burning incense stick told me I was right. The monks started the closing rituals, and I started to count my breaths as the instructions say. As the monk hit the wooden clappers to signal the end, I wondered at how short and relatively pain-free the sitting actually had been. For the first time ever, I felt I wanted to and could sit longer. As I turned on my knees to get up, my legs were still painful, and I had to wait the usual few minutes before standing. When I did, it was easier, though. I had hit a new plateau.

Sitting To Lengthen the Spine

Both Ida and Moshe had taught that any good exercise lengthened the spine. So I was convinced that if this painful exercise produced any good results, it had to lengthen the spine whatever else it did. The sitter should grow straighter and taller as he sat. So when I was not counting my breaths, looking at my pain, or working to get 180 degree vision, I was working to extend my spine.

My spine had become too rounded through the rib cage and too flat through the lumbar area. Years and gravity had taken their toll, shortening and compressing my spine. Of course, my head had to be too far forward in order to compensate and give my spine its aberrated balance. I wanted to flatten the upper spine, put more curve in the lower spine, and get my head back over the body.

I knew that the extensors and flexors of the trunk had to be balanced to allow the iliopsoas and the intrinsic muscles connecting the vertebrae to lift the spine. I figured that since the psoas connects to the transverse spine and also to the base of each vertebra beginning from under the diaphragm and continuing throughout the pelvic vertebrae, a force pulling from these two points on each vertebra can change the angle between each vertebra. This action, combined with the hydraulic action induced by the small intrinsic muscles pressuring the gel of the discs, can powerfully lift the spine.

The action of these muscles is coordinated through breathing. On the exhalation the psoas and the muscles of the back pull the pelvis forward and tighten the lower abdomen. The spine is lengthened by the increased pressure in the gel of the vertebrae. On the inhalation the psoas and the back muscles relax, and the air rushes in and lifts the rib cage.

Tanouye Roshi says to think of your lower belly as a balloon. If you hold and squeeze the center of the balloon, the balloon becomes longer. This is the way the spine extends when the lower belly is tightened as the exhalation is slowly pushed out, and the lungs completely emptied. During this process my spine sometimes pops and cracks, Like the cap popping off a plastic ketchup bottle when you squeeze it hard enough. The inhalation seems to be just a letting go, and the air rushes in and lifts the rib cage and the spine with it. Interestingly the shoulders do not go up. It is just the spine lifting through the shoulder girdle without any noticeable effect on the shoulders. It is a great feeling to differentiate the shoulder girdle from the movement of the spine.

I know my spine has more flexibility and length now. I know that I take more air in and out than before. I can sit on the floor with more ease and get up and down looking less like a wounded buffalo. I weighed 225 pounds when I first came to Chozen-ji; now I weigh twenty pounds less. My posture also improved; instead of aberrating my hip joints and lower back, sitting took some of the knock out of my knees and put some curve in my flat lower back. My kinesthetic sensitivity increased as zazen eliminated the random movements which mask the intricate workings of the body. Most importantly, however, zazen cultivated my vital energy and enabled me to touch clients at a deeper level.

The Hawaiian Mystic

One day Alvin and Audrey came into the dojo supporting a frail woman between them. She seemed quite ill and looked worn out. I got her down on the table and worked her body for about an hour. I worked at clearing the trigger points in the neck, back, and chest. She was really in the "here and now" with me, and she released the points almost as soon as I could find them.

Tanouye Roshi came into the hall, but he was not dressed in his customary blue coveralls. He was wearing his formal robes and carrying a ceremonial wand with a tuft of long white hairs. He went to the altar and performed various rituals. Then he came over to our table and made some passes with the wand before sitting at the foot of the table and feeding energy into the lady via her feet.

There was a supernatural stillness in the air that morning. Four of us stood near the door watching in hushed silence. The lady began to chant in Hawaiian in a man's voice. Then it was as if powerful lights had been turned on and flooded the room with their brightness. Alvin turned to me and whispered, "I can't stand this stuff," and he rushed out the door. The light and the chanting continued for some time.

Then Tanouye Roshi went to her head, performed a ritual, and said, "You are freed of your trust. You no longer need to find a successor. You are free." Later Tanouye Roshi told me that it was not he who was speaking but that the words had just come to him.

The woman got up from the table. She was lit up like a light bulb. She walked a few feet in front of us and, looking into open space, gave a speech. Her voice was loud and strong, as if she was talking to a crowd. I remember that the first few sentences did not make sense to me, and I thought that the poor old lady had flipped her lid. Then what she was saying began to make sense. Then I began to feel the wisdom of her words about the spirit of aloha. I felt a love and affinity for this lady and, through her, a love for all mankind. I cried.

When she was finished, she thanked Tanouye Roshi and walked to the car unassisted. The lady was Pilahi Paki, one of the most revered of the Hawaiian spiritual teachers and shamans. She died not long after.

In the spring session of 1986, the Hawaii State Legislature adopted her definition of aloha as "the working philosophy of Hawaii." Pilahi taught:

"Aloha Spirit" is the coordination of mind and heart . . . it's within the individual—it brings you down to yourself. You must think and emote good feelings to others.

- A - stands for *akahai* meaning kindness, to be expressed with wisdom.
- L - stands for *lokahi* meaning unity, to be expressed with harmony.
- O - stands for *olu'olu* meaning agreeable, to be expressed with pleasantness.
- H - stands for *ha'aha'a* meaning humility, to be expressed with modesty.
- A - stands for *ahonui* meaning patience, to be expressed with perseverance.

100

Sending Energy Through the Feet

Usually the Zen Bodytherapist will send energy into a client by holding his feet while he lies on his back with his arms at his side. One day Tanouye Roshi came in while I was trying to do this and suggested I try sending my energy through the thick wooden walls of the dojo. I went to the wall and pushed slightly with my fingers. He asked if I was able to push my energy through the wall, and I said no. He asked me how far it was going. I said not very far. He came over and put his hand on top of mine and them asked me if it was getting through the wall. I felt it go through the wall and far beyond. He withdrew his hand, and I felt I was still going through the wall. He said to recreate this same feeling whenever I fed energy into someone.

The next morning a doctor with a heart problem came to the dojo. Tanouye Roshi told me to work the left arm, the left side of the chest and around the base of the neck. He then left for the rest of the morning. I quickly worked these areas, and then since the master was not around, I went down the body looking for areas that might block the flow of energy from his feet. When this was done, I sat down and placed my hands over his feet and toes, try-ing to recreate the feeling of pushing through the wall. It was not long before the doctor was breathing heavily and was fast asleep. For twenty minutes I held the position while he slept. I was quite disgusted that he fell asleep while I was working. He got up saying he felt much better and we both went to our jobs.

I returned to the dojo later that day and found Tanouye Roshi and the doctor talking. The Zen Master motioned me to join them and then asked the doctor to retell his story. The doctor said that while he was seemingly asleep, he had been fully awake and alert, seeing colors and experiencing a great feeling of aliveness and well-being. After he had finished his story, Tanouye Roshi turned to me and said, "That is what they call *samadhi*."

Freeing the Breath with Energy

He was a fat, jolly professional man in his early sixties with a his-tory of being in and out of the hospital with heart problems. I had been told that he could go at any time. He had been experiencing difficulty breathing for three or four days and came puffing into my office. Each breath was an effort, a real struggle. He took his clothes off and lay down on the table. There was no movement in his upper rib cage. I worked his stiff neck and the occipital ridge of the skull. I made sure the blood was moved down from his head and neck into the trunk. As I did this, the bluish-purple color of his face turned pinkish. I hoped his blood pressure went down as his color changed.

Then I moved down to the rib cage. Under the arm pits on both sides were many hot trigger points. A trigger point is a medical term referring to a place where toxins have accumulated so that when pressure is applied, the pain is often triggered or referred to another part of the body. They were quite slow to disappear but eventually did. Once the sides were cleared, I moved up to the front of the chest and then the back of the chest, relaxing the tight muscles, and slowly clearing off the hot trigger points. While working the back, I worked the twelfth rib and the crest of the pelvic bones (ilium). This would normally get the ribs moving and improve the breathing. Today, however, there was no noticeable improvement.

By this time an hour had passed, so I decided to change the approach and send energy through his feet. After I held the toes and feet with my hands for about ten minutes, he said he could feel the energy going just to the knees. I bent his leg and worked the front and back and then worked the other leg the same way. Then I went to the spaces between the bones on the top of the feet and cleaned out the trigger points there.

Again I sat holding his toes and feet in my hands, and this time the energy went up the legs through the pelvis and into the chest. He began to cough and spit out phlegm. He did this intermittently for the next hour during which he described beautiful colors and pictures similar to what he experienced during meditation. He kept falling asleep for short periods of time only to wake up coughing. As the phlegm came out, his breathing became more normal except for his nose which was still plugged up. I moved to this hands and opened up the spaces between the bones in the front of the right hand, and the right nostril opened up. After I worked on his left hand, the left nostril opened up. After two hours on the table, he had a pink face and said that he felt quite good.

Working Intuitively

She said everything was wrong. She had arthritis throughout her body, bloated up whenever she ate, and on and on. After listening to her long list of ailments, I wondered about working her. Then instead of asking her to undress as usual, without thinking about it, I picked up her right hand and started working the worst looking, most painful joint. Instead of going away as I had expected, the pain got greater. She reported that not only did her finger joint hurt, but also her shoulder, then her arm. and then her neck. The pattern kept changing and moving around. The whole show fascinated me, and I knew I could learn something from this woman.

I asked her to take her clothes off except for her underwear and to lie on her back. I started working her neck which was tight but which relaxed under my hands. As I worked her neck, I noticed an odd pattern throughout the anterior trunk. It was pulling in from all sides toward the middle, as if her body wanted to fold in half. I moved to the chest muscles and the tension there confirmed my observation. Next I checked her belly, which was large and quite muscular, compared to the rest of her body, and it too seemed to want to help the body to fold.

I started to lengthen the muscles in the front of the chest. This triggered a series of convulsions with the body trying to fold in on itself. All of the flexor muscles of the front were strained and contracted during these convulsions. They stopped after a few minutes, and I gave her a needed rest for a while. Once again I started working the muscle attachments in the front of the chest, and she went into convulsions again.

This time I grabbed the tissue in the center of her belly, (the rectus abdominis muscles), with both my hands and squeezed as tight as I could. Holding these muscles counteracted the impulse of her body to shorten and fold. She tried a few times, then gave up, and the convulsions stopped. I worked the chest again; she started to convulse but failed because I held her abdominal muscles. After a few more trials, working her chest did not trigger convulsions, and the pattern was broken.

I moved to her back and found that the muscles through the lumbar were very tight, flat, and immovable. I lengthened the adductors on both legs and the abdominal rectus and then worked both psoas muscles as well. Now her pelvis was structurally capable of turning or rocking forward and back, but she still could not move her pelvis. Her nervous system did not have the wiring to perform these movements. I began helping her develop the necessary awareness by manually manipulating her pelvis while she experienced the movement with their hands. It took a while, but she finally acquired the new circuits in her gray matter which enabled her to move her pelvis.

I then asked her how her sex life was and she said, "So, so." I asked if that meant she had none of it or it was not too good. She said that it was not that good. I explained the mechanics of orgasm to her, how the muscles of the pelvis must participate in the movement and the release of the orgasm. She left the session feeling light, happy, and eager to try out her new pelvis.

I saw her for two more sessions. The first time she came back she said that her life, especially her sex life, had changed greatly for the better. The second time it was easy to see that her outlook and experience of life were stabilized at a much higher level.

This is a good example of using many techniques but no plan. I made moves that my old teachers would have disapproved of, but by working intuitively I got the job done. Rolfing would have taken about ten to twenty hours; Feldenkrais maybe twenty of thirty sessions. Yet by doing this Rolf technique here, this Functional Integration manipulation there, this improvisation now— but all according to the principles of circulating energy—I facilitated the woman's transformation in a remarkably short period. At the end, her hands and feet were warmer and her head cooler; her blood and energy were flowing much more freely than before. From complaining about her ailments she moved to enjoying her body and her life.

Audrey

Whenever someone comes to see Tanouye Roshi about learning to do healing, he discourages them, telling them that it is a life-shortening, painful, hard, low-paying, and unappreciated job. Only reluctantly will he accept people to train as healers. Audrey was one who persisted in spite of all discouragement.

After work one day, I felt ill and asked Audrey if she would work me and clean me out. She put her hands on the front of my chest and I started to cough. Audrey's body, especially her arms and shoulders, shook frantically. This went on for some minutes and then subsided. She then moved her hands a few inches and the drama was repeated. She continued doing this until my chest had been covered from the front. After the process was finished on the throat, she turned me over and put her hands on the back. The effect was the same. After this area was cleared, I felt quite well, my energy had returned and I was no longer tired. My wheezing had disappeared. My mood was light and optimistic.

A short time later Audrey complained of pain in her legs. When I asked her where the pain was, she pointed to the area at the top of the upper thigh (the anterior superior spine area) and down the adductor muscles.

I was surprised and told her of the client who had poisoned me that day. She had serious leg problems and walked with a cane. Even though she was only in her late twenties, her body, especially the legs, were loaded with poison. I coughed, choked, stopped, washed and even left the room a time or two as I attempted to work her upper legs. I finally stopped and had her try her legs. She said there was some improvement, but I told her that I could not finish the hour and suggested she contact a local spiritual healer to see if some of the poison could be exorcised. She agreed to do this and left.

I remained sick and wheezing until Audrey worked me. The work she did with me differed form the work I did with my poisonous client. Audrey used straight vital energy and no pressure. I used considerable pressure and, of course, used vital energy incidentally as I had my awareness in the pressure I exerted on the hard, short connective tissue in my client's legs.

About two years ago I returned to San Francisco to find one of my "little old lady" clients ailing. I called her and asked if I could bring a couple of unorthodox healers to work on her. The client was very ill, yet gracious and happy to have us work on her. Audrey was in San Francisco visiting her sister, so I took her and Laurie, another healer and bodyworker, to visit this client.

She showed Audrey her arthritic hands with knobby joints and asked her to work on them while Laurie and I worked the rest of the body. Years ago when the client was having trouble closing her hands and holding onto things, I had worked her fingers and taught her how to work her own hands. Her ability to use her fingers greatly improved as she faithfully worked her hands daily. The knuckles, however, did not reduce much in size. She always seemed embarrassed about her knobby knuckles.

We got her feeling better, and a few days later, I returned to work her body once again before my return to Hawaii.

About a week later I received a phone call from this excited lady, "You should see my hands, they are beautiful—just like they used to be." I asked if the knuckles were still enlarged or knobby and she said, "No!" They were just smooth, beautiful and young. I said that I could not believe it. She said that she could not either. She asked me a number of times, "What did she do to my hands?"

She said she was on a trip with her husband. I never did get to see her beautifully changed hands.

REVERSING THE AGING PROCESS

FOR ME aging is:

Getting rigid in thoughts and actions.
Poorer hearing, sight, taste, and touch.
Saying, "I'm too old for that."
Developing hard, tight, short muscles.
Having less strength, energy, and mobility.
Aching and complaining more and more often.
Shrinking and losing height.

Aging is not just having another birthday. Chronological age does not strictly correlate with aging. Fries and Crapo of the Stanford University School of Medicine write:

By any standard of aging we choose to use, we age at different rates, and the differences between us grow greater as we grow older! The different rates again prove, in one sense, that chronological age itself is not a good marker for aging. In a more profound sense, however, increasing variation with age suggests that there must be a reason for the differences. If we could understand the reasons, we might be able to exchange a rapid rate of aging for a slower one—we might be able to postpone the aging process.[1]

Many factors influence the aging process: world and national events, diet, physical activity, family, job, social position, sex, and retirement, to name a few. Long-term studies are needed to isolate key variables and determine their effects on the aging process. We already know, however, that by focusing on the structure, function, and energy of the person, much can be done to improve men-

107

tal function, physical function, and social function within very broad biological limits.

This will become increasingly important because we are living longer thanks to medical and technological advances. We must make sure, however, that this additional time is not a prolongation of dying but an extension of living.

The ideal is not to live as long as possible but to live as fully as possible so that death is the celebration of a life fully spent. In this case, all parts of the body entropy evenly together; organs and tissue disintegrate in unison. The time of adult vigor would increase, and time spent in dependency and infirmity would decrease. In the end death would be a natural transition to a higher level of being and an affirmation of life.

Thomas Hanna writes:

Because all of us are of certain age, it will be to our betterment if we keep clearly in mind that although the annihilation of death is unavoidable, the presumed disintegration of aging is quite avoidable. It is avoidable because the process of living does not necessarily have anything to do with disintegration. The belief that aging is a disintegration leading directly to death is purely a myth. But it is a vicious and destructive myth —a myth which, if accepted and believed in, fulfills itself with almost certain disintegration. Because it is a self-fulfilling prophecy, "aging" is the greatest single factor in the cause of death. Or, expressed less whimsically, the myth of aging is a self-destructive aspect of contemporary culture that sponsors human disintegration and annihilation.

But perhaps worse than this, the myth of aging portrays human life, in effect, as meaningless and futile. It denies that life is growth, that life can be adventurous, open-ended, and creative. It denies that human life can go forward, developing outward toward increasing fulfillment. The myth of aging denies the very essence of young age's enthusiastic development by suggesting that the ultimate trajectory of youth is disintegration and non-fulfillment. Because life is a single span of time, beginning with birth and ending with death, one cannot denigrate one age of living without denigrating the whole of living.[2]

The life cycle starts with an uninhibited baby, living freely in each moment of the here and now, inquisitive, learning and growing, and building new patterns of movement and thought. Most of these patterns, whether productive or not, are seldom, if ever, looked at or changed.

During our younger years we are molded physically, mentally, and spiritually. As we enter our middle years, our lives and our bodies are less receptive to changes. Our patterns become increasingly rigid and restrictive. Nine to five we spend at work; six to eleven watching television; and weekends watching, not playing, ballgames. Our posture and patterns of movement are the same at work and at home with a few uncomfortable exceptions, and daily deeper ruts are cut into our bodies and brains.

When we try to do a new movement, our bodies creak and complain with pain. We say, "I must be getting old," when it would be more accurate to say, "I'm getting rusty from lack of use." Each year our overall movements are fewer and smaller. We forget that what we don't use, we tend to lose.

By now in our life the connective tissue has become short, brittle, and somewhat calcified. The joints are pulled tight and constricted, making painless movement almost impossible. Trauma and stress have been stored and stored in layer after layer, leading to trigger points and inhibited organs. There are malfunctions and pains, and we slide downhill into death.

It does not have to be this way. Bodytherapy can help us to enjoy vibrancy and gracefulness throughout life. It can help us release the aberrations from past physical and emotional trauma which block our flow of vital energy. Bodytherapy can do this by increasing the awareness and movement of your body, by physical pressure and manipulation, by receiving energy from another person, or by all of these methods. When old, dried-up tissue becomes bouncy, soft, and elastic, when awkward, impaired movement becomes smooth and easy, haven't we reversed the aging process?

I have seen this happen with many clients. On one occasion I found a little old lady hanging on the railing on the stair landing to my office. I want down and helped her up the last few steps and into the nearest available room where she lay down on the table. Her color and breathing caused me much concern. She said, "When my husband called, he did not tell you I have a heart problem." She also told me she was eighty-three years old.

I loosened her clothing and gently worked her neck. After a few minutes I told her that I could not Rolf her and doubted I could be of service to her. But as I worked down into the rib cage, I noted

109

that she seemed greatly relieved, and her breathing improved. When she got ready to leave, she asked if she could come again and have me do some more work. We agreed that I would do some light Feldenkrais work with her. She came in every week for a few months, getting Feldenkrais and deep tissue work, and then went to her medical doctor for a physical.

The doctor could not understand how her tissue had changed from hard, thick, tight tissue to soft, resilient, long fibers. He kept sticking his fingers into the young, bouncy tissue and commenting that he could not understand the change in her body. He advised her to continue doing whatever she was doing. So I kept working with her for seven years until she left the area.

One day I had a twenty-five-year-old lady come into the office right after I finished working with the older woman. The young woman was an ex-drug abuser. I was startled by the contrast in their bodies. The tissue of the young woman was hard, drawn-up short, brittle, and stringy, while the tissue of the older woman was soft, resilient, alive, and a joy to touch.

Another client was an eighty-year-old woman who was under a doctor's care for many physical problems. She had trouble breathing whenever she exerted herself at all. Her stomach often refused to handle the food she ate. She had chronic pain and tightness throughout her body but especially on the left side of the ribs.

Nevertheless, she loved life and people and was interested in everything. She was extremely bright, observant, and "young in mind." I soon developed a love for her and enjoyed being around her. I wanted to do the best work I could for her.

Slowly her breathing improved so she could go up a full flight of stairs without resting or puffing. She could handle food better, and the chronic pain went away. Once she reached this plateau she stayed there with little change for about five years. It became evident to her, me, and everyone who knew her history that the bodytherapy was keeping her functioning. She used to say, "Dub, you are keeping me alive." She felt better each time I worked her. The ribs would soften and move gently and freely with each breath. The hard deep contractions felt in the stomach area would disappear, likewise the tender spot where the 12th rib joins the vertebra. The large muscles of the back and neck lengthed and softened. She would get up from the table feisty and sharp, and I would tell her she was good for another week.

It seemed like it happened almost overnight. She began failing. She noticed the quick changes much more than I did, "Dub, look at my breasts and skin. They have become so old overnight. They are the skin and breasts of an old, old lady." The pain in her back and belly came back. At first I could get it out, and it would stay out for a few days. Then each week it returned sooner. Finally I could not get all the pain out, and it was a continuous problem to handle food. She lost weight quickly and died. Her death was very unexpected for her family, but she and I knew she died so quickly because she had lived so fully and was ready to die.

Some years ago Moshe brought Margaret Mead into our training class at Lone Mountain College. He explained that they were planning a center on the East Coast that would be an ideal environment for himself, Margaret, and other people in their sixties or older who wanted to continue productive activity and to extend their life in the most optimal manner. Exercises in movement and awareness along with bodywork were to be the keys to reaching this goal. Margaret passed away before Moshe returned to the East Coast to implement their plan. Since that time, however, I have not been able to forget the thought of building a facility to utilize our knowledge of how to reverse the aging process.

I envision a multi-story building with lots of windows. There are easy access ramps leading up to large double doors. The doors open for me, and I step inside. I feel a warm welcome. I think that it must be the warm earthy colors and textures.

A grandmother with white hair walks by talking to the smiling baby she is holding. I follow them into a room which looks like a lobby. There are a few chairs and sofas along the wall, but everyone, men, women, and children, are on the floor with their shoes off. I slip my shoes off and kick them under a chair. I sit down on the floor and watch the people of all ages play with each other. They are interacting just for the fun of it. All of them, including the elderly, are crawling, rolling, stretching, lying, bending, and enjoying the whole range of movements.

I notice a young lady massaging an infant, and two teenagers gleefully digging their elbows into the back of a tall, gray-haired

111

man as he lies face down on a sheet. Soft classical music plays in the background. Everyone is having fun.

I ask where all the babies and children come from. I am told that single-parent families, especially unwed mothers, are invited to live here. They can work and go to the college which is within walking distance, and their children are cared for while they are away.

I am told that everyone who lives here works, either in the nursery, the school, the laundry, the kitchen, the dining room, the gym, the pool, or the office, or maintains the building and grounds. Everyone is responsible for some part of the overall functioning and for supporting others in getting their work done. Jobs change when a person masters a job.

When I ask about living quarters, I learn that each family has their apartment or suite, a sound-proof, private, and safe place to retreat to when appropriate or desired.

I ask for an application to move in.

This may be just a dream for now, but I can testify to the reality of reversing the aging process from my own experience.

Four years ago in 1982 I passed out in my office. I could not remember where I was. As I reached out, I felt something smooth and cold. Then I realized I was lying curled up on my side. Everything seemed very strange. I could not remember where I was or how I got there. Even when my eyes began to focus, I remained in a quandary. Finally I realize that I was lying on the floor, in my office, half under my desk. My hand had touched the cold, smooth metal of the toppled office chair. With a struggle I pulled myself to my feet, using the desk for support.

Then I remembered that one moment I had been sitting at my desk and the next moment I was lying on the floor. How long I had been there, I did not know.

As I started to laugh, the phone rang. It was a client who happened to be a medical doctor. I laughingly told him what had happened and commented on how easy it would have been to finish my life at that moment. He did not understand the humor of the incident, and after asking me a lot of questions about my health, said he would call his cousin at the clinic and arrange for me to be admitted immediately.

112

They got me down to the clinic, and after a battery of tests the doctor sat me down and said I had double pneumonia. For the first time in some twenty odd years, I had to take medicine.

I was surprised at how slowly my health returned, even after I stopped taking the medicine. Considering what I had done with my body during the last year, I should not have been surprised.

It was just about a year since my sister had been taken to the San Jose hospital with terminal cancer. She died two months later and left an invalid husband. During that year, I attempted to keep my office open and running, live with and take care of my brother-in-law in Livermore while assisting my sister through her terminal illness. While my sister was in the hospital, I would spend a couple of hours at the office in San Francisco, then drive to the hospital in San Jose, and stay with my sister until night when I drove to Livermore to tend to my brother-in-law. The morning meant a fight to get over the bridge to my office for a couple of hours before repeating the cycle. So it went until I collapsed onto the floor.

It was then that for the first time in my life, I felt old. My joints were stiff. It was an effort to move one foot ahead of the other. I just wanted to sit and not move. I did not give a damn about anything. My powers of recuperation seemed to be gone. Day after day there was little improvement. Life had become a burden. It was a heavy effort to do anything. A small cut in the skin never seemed to heal. Breathing was an effort.

It was in this state that I started coming to Hawaii in 1983. I had given up most of my clients and lost interest in body work. In 1984 I met Tanouye Roshi, and he rekindled my passion to understand the body and to serve others. He opened up the whole new field of vital energy for me. I learned how it circulates, how it relates to life, health, and death, and how I could use it on clients that had previously stumped me and my limited knowledge. I began to work more clients with renewed interest. I set up a full schedule and made time afterwards to study and have my own body worked. I regained my health and began functioning as if I were years younger.

Today in 1986, four years after I collapsed in my old office, I am older in years and younger in age. Five days per week, I get up at five in the morning, take a fast mile walk to and from Chozen-ji where I sit zazen for a half hour. It is not an effort. In fact, when the downhill slope gets steep, I jog until the path becomes flat again. I find working clients enjoyable and reasonably easy. I go to sleep quickly and sleep soundly. I have no aches or pains, except when I sit zazen. I enjoy social interaction. Keeping house, cooking, doing laundry, and grocery-shopping are not unpleasant chores. I am healthy according to Moshe who said that a healthy man needed to be productive, happy doing whatever he was doing, and have a good sex life. I look forward to each day and can't finish all the things I want to do. Although I never wrote much before, I am in the process of writing three training manuals and finishing this book for the tenth and, I trust, final time.

At the age of seventy-two, I am rejuvenated and living life anew.

APPENDIX

Exercises for Reversing the Aging Process

When you do these exercises, wear loose clothing and remember that these instructions are usually given by a teacher to a group. You may find it useful to tape these instructions for yourself, or you can have someone read while you do the movements. Be sure to leave long pauses between instructions.

Exercises done on the floor can be most comfortably done if you place a sheet on a carpeted floor. Exercises done while standing are easiest to do if you can stand in front of two mirrors placed perpendicular to each other, but even a single mirror will help greatly.

Do not expect much result from the Rolf girdle exercises unless you do these exercises at least four times weekly. They are best done each work day. To do these exercises only two or three times weekly is a waste of time. Ida's exercise to lengthen the spine and Moshe's exercises, however, can be done anytime, anywhere as long as they are done slowly and with awareness. They will produce results.

Ida's Exercise for Sitting and Lengthening while Standing

Stand with your feet apart the same width as your hip joint and keep them parallel and pointing straight forward. Let your arms hang at your sides, thumbs against the thighs with the elbows pointing away from the body.

Say to yourself, "Sit from the groin, letting the knees go straight forward as the waistline goes back." After a short pause in this position, say to yourself, "Now let the top of my head lift me back up." Repeat this every time you do the exercise.

The waist line is the normal line of the belt, and to take the waist back means that the shoulders and the hips stay put and the waist line, the lumbars, flatten and move toward the rear of the body. Now, the top of the head is that spot where the bones join on the exterior superior part of the skull. If you stick your index fingers in your ears and then slide them up the side over the top of the skull until they meet at the midline, you will locate the top of your head. Remember this spot so you can put your finger and awareness there whenever necessary.

Stand in front of a full-length mirror. This will help you to perform the appropriate movement. Stand with your feet parallel to each other. Now move your knees straight forward and back slowly, looking at the space between the knees. As this space changes, the rotation of the knee can be seen. If the kneecap and the feet point in different directions, the legs are twisted between the knees and the feet. Work at keeping the space even and the knees and feet pointed in the same direction; sit while moving your waistline back. Then imagine that a hook lifts you from the tip of the head and aligns your body with the gravitational field of the Earth.

Remain in the uplifted position for a few moments or even a minute or two and imagine yourself growing even taller. You will be able to experience where up is and what your body's structure is when aligned with the Earth's gravitational field.

Ida's Exercise for Organizing the Lower Girdle

Sit with your back against a wall or the back of a partner. Bend your left knee, pulling your heel close to your buttocks. Make sure your back, especially the sacrum, is flat against its support. Extend your right leg straight forward with the back of the leg lying flat on the floor.

Point your right foot and toes toward the ceiling and at right angles to the floor. Hold your foot motionless and move your toes back and forth. Keeping your foot motionless, turn your toes down as if grasping a pencil. With your toes grasping the imaginary pencil, move the bottom of your foot straight down toward the floor.

After you move your foot down as far as possible, still holding

116

the pencil and keeping your toes, foot, and leg aligned, bring your foot up as far as possible. With your foot up and still holding the pencil, step down with your heel and lengthen your leg. Then move your foot down still holding the pencil.

Hold your foot down and bring your toes up, dropping the pencil. Keep your toes up and bring your foot up. Keep both up and push your heel toward the far wall; this move will straighten and lengthen your leg.

Now, keeping your toes up, move your foot down—now hold your foot down and take your toes down. Take a deep breath and relax. See if you can feel how the body begins to organize itself as you do Ida's exercise.

Ida's Shoulder Girdle Exercise

Lie on your back, draw up your knees, and keep the soles of your feet on the floor. Put your arms palm down along your sides. Now slide your arms up from your sides until they are at right angles to your body, and extend your hands straight out reaching out from the shoulder joint.

Continuing to reach out from the shoulder joint, bring your arms up over your chest with the back of your hands going toward each other until your arms are parallel and straight out from the shoulder joint. Lift your scapulas (shoulder blades) off the floor by extending your hands further toward the ceiling. Now let the shoulder blades drop back to the floor. Still reaching out with your hands, let your arms slowly go down toward the floor but do not let them touch the floor.

Now, reach out further with your arms from the shoulder joint, and turn your arm a quarter of a circle so your thumbs point toward the ceiling. Throughout this exercise all the turning is done in the shoulder joint and not in the wrist or elbow. Now bring your arms up over your chest again, this time with your thumbs coming toward each other. Stop when the arms are parallel over the chest. Continuing to reach out, slowly let your arms go down with the cutting edge of your hands leading the way toward the floor. Do not touch the floor.

Reach out again and turn a quarter of a circle from the shoulder joint so your palms are facing the ceiling. Now bring the palms toward each other over your chest. Stop when the arms are straight over the chest and are parallel to each other. Again slowly bring your arms down, this time with the backs of your hands toward the floor, but do not touch the floor.

Now turn the arm from the shoulder joint so that the cutting edges of your hands face the ceiling. Bring the two cutting edges toward each other over the chest, reaching out as you do this. After the arms are straight and parallel over the shoulder joints, slowly bring the two thumbs down toward the floor, but do not touch the floor.

This completes one half of the cycle, and the process will now be reversed to complete the other half. Reach out from the shoulder joint, but do not rotate the arm this time. Just take the cutting edges of the hands toward each other over the chest. After you bring your arms over the shoulders, slowly take your thumbs toward the floor, but do not touch the floor.

Now, reaching out from the shoulder joint, rotate the arm a quarter of a circle so the palms of the hand face the ceiling. Bring the hands toward each other over the chest. Take the back of your hands down toward the floor. Stop just before getting to the floor.

Rotate the arm from the shoulder joint a quarter of a circle so the thumbs point toward the ceiling. Bring them toward each other over the chest. Take the cutting edge of your hands down toward the floor, stopping just before you reach the floor.

Reach out and rotate your arm from the shoulder joint so the backs of your hands face the ceiling. Bring the backs of your hands toward each other over your chest. Take your arms toward the floor palms down and let your palms touch the floor.

Now reaching out with your arms and sliding your palms along the floor, bring your arms to your sides. Reach down with your hands and imagine that twenty pound weights hold each hand in place. Then slowly take your elbow straight out about four or five inches. Relax!

Moshe's Eye Exercises

Lie on your back and make yourself comfortable. Your knees can be bent, or your legs can be extended. Close your eyes.

Place the fleshy part of the palm of your right hand over your right eye. Put just enough pressure on the eyeball so you can feel the movement of the eyeball. Move your eyeball to the left, as if you were looking at something over to your left. Then bring the eyeball back to center. Move it back to the left again and back to center again. Do this many times.

Now stop that, and this time look to your right. Feel your eyeball move to the right under the eyelid. Bring your eyeball back to the center again. Then move it back to the right and back to center again. Repeat this movement many times.

Now stop that, and move your eyeball forward as if you were looking at your toes. Take the eyeball back to the center. Repeat this movement many times.

Now stop that, and take your eye up as if you were looking at your eyebrow. Move the eye back to the center. Do this movement many times.

Now take the eyeball down as far as you can and then back through the center and up as far as it will go. Repeat the movement many times.

Look to the left, and then back through the center to the right as far as you can. Repeat this many times. Make sure your hand can feel the movement of the eyeball from side to side.

Leaving your eyes closed, rest your hand for a few moments. After a short pause, put your hand back over your eye so the fleshy part of the hand once again rests lightly on your right eyeball.

Now move the eye in a circle clockwise, making the circle as large as possible. After doing this briefly, make the circle very small and the movement very fast. Make a lot of tiny circles. Then make some very large circles again.

Stop that, and make large circles in the opposite direction. Now make the small circles and make them fast. Stop that and make a few large circles.

Change the circle into a square. Make four square corners and four flat sides. Make large squares.

Reverse the direction the eyeball is moving and make more large squares.

When you come to a corner in the square, make a diagonal line across the square to the opposite corner. Then move on to another corner of the square and make another diagonal line. Continue to repeat this movement: make a diagonal, move your eyeball down one side to another corner, and make another diagonal. Now change direction and continue doing the same thing. Feel the movement of your eyeball on your hand.

Keeping your eyes closed, remove your hand from your eye. Put your awareness in the right side of your face. Compare the right with the left side of your face. Sense the lines around the outside edge of the right eye and compare them with the same area around the left eye. Are they different? Does one eye feel larger and more relaxed than the other? Sense the corners of your mouth kinesthetically. Can you discern a difference? Does the left side of the face feel very different from the right?

Now open your eyes, roll over and stand up. Get a partner and look at the two halves of each other's faces. Share what you see. If you are alone, look in a mirror to see the differences in the two sides.

Close your eyes. Do the two shoulders feel different? Can you feel a difference in the two sides of the body? Open your eyes and see if you can discern any difference in your partner.

Good, now lie back down on the floor. Place the palm of your left hand on your left eye. Move your eyeball to the left, but only your left eyeball. If you place your right hand over your right eye, you will find that moving just the left eye is almost impossible because the eyes move naturally together. All along you have been moving both eyes together through the exercise.

Both eyes have been moving in the same fashion, and yet one eye and one side of the face and body are definitely different and more relaxed. The difference lies in the awareness with which the movements of the right eye were performed compared to the lack of awareness in the movements of the left eye. *Awareness is the difference between calisthenics and Feldenkrais exercises.* When performed with awareness, movements are integrated into the nervous system and change the functioning of the body.

Now repeat the various movements you performed on the right side, on the left side this time. But do the whole routine in your imagination. Move the eyeball in your mind's eye only, and balance your two sides.

Moshe's Exercise for Lengthening by Twisting

Stand with your feet straight ahead, parallel to each other and spread apart the distance between the two hip joints. Raise your right hand to your eye level as if to see the time on a wrist watch. Hold your arm in that position as you turn your body to the right. Do not move your feet; just turn your body to the right as far as is comfortable, pleasant, and without strain. When you have gone as far as is comfortable without strain, raise your eyes straight up and look beyond the watch to see where the line of vision falls on the far wall. Mark this point as a reference for comparison later.

After you have marked this point, turn your body back to the center and drop your arm to your side. Now close your eyes, and turn your body to the right. Holding your body there to the right, turn only your head back to the center and then back again to the right. Your body stays turned to the right. Just the head moves to the center and back to the right many times. Feel the movement, the twist throughout your body. Feel the difference in the two feet, the two legs, the two sides of the pelvis, the rib cage; note the bones of the neck. Now stop that and return the body to the front. Take a deep breath and let it out.

Now turn your body back to the right. This time, keeping your head and body turned to the right, move only your eyes back to center then to the right. Repeat many times. Scan your body as you do this. Is your whole body participating in the movement? Feel how everything interconnects. Make small movements with your eyes, faster and faster, smaller and smaller. Stop that and make the movement graceful and easy. Bring your head and body back to the center and take a couple of deep breaths.

Once again turn your body, head and closed eyes to the right just as far as comfortable. Keeping your head and eyes to the right, bring your shoulder back to the center and then to the right. Only the trunk and shoulder move. Make the movement an easy one. Do not push the movement. Do not strain. Make the movement as pleasant and graceful as possible. Note how the twist goes through the entire body. Stop that and bring everything back to the center. Take a deep breath, lift your shoulders to your ears, and drop them as you exhale, and now again.

Open your eyes, lift your right arm, and look at the imaginary wrist watch as you turn to the right, just as far as is comfortable and pleasant, just as you did before. When you stop, lift your eyes from the watch to the wall and see where your line of vision hits the wall. How much farther can you turn compared with the first time you measured? Measure this difference with your two hands.

Close your eyes again; bring everything back to center with your arms at your sides, and just scan your body comparing the two sides. Which one feels longer? Which one is more relaxed? Compare the feet, legs, pelvis, shoulders, back, ribs, neck, and head. Do you want the other side worked?

Turn your body comfortably to the left and mark a point on the wall looking over an imaginary watch on your left hand. Come back to center, close your eyes, and drop your hand.

From here on you are going to work in your imagination only. Do not move your body in the real world. Just imagine doing the movements. The movements you will do in your imagination on this side are duplications of the movements you just experienced doing on the right side. The left brain has recorded the experience as done by the right side. Now you are going to transfer that experience to the right brain and relay it to the nervous system, muscles, and connective tissue of the left side of your body.

Without moving in the real world, in your imagination only, turn your body, head, and eyes all to the left. Keep your feet planted in the original position. In your imagination, hold the body to the left and turn your head to the center and back to the left many times. Note how you can do the movement faster and always perfectly.

Stop that and in your imagination, keeping the body and the head turned to the left, bring the eyes back to center and return to the left many times. In your imagination, make the movement ever faster and smaller. Do this many times.

Stop that and this time while the eyes and head are being held to the left, move the shoulder and trunk of the body back to the center and then return it to the left. Do this many times. In your imagination only re-experience the same experience you had when this movement was done on the right side. Note the corresponding feelings and strains. Now in your imagination bring your entire body back to the center.

Keeping your eyes closed, take a couple of deep breaths and let them out as you lift your shoulders and drop them. Great. Now with your eyes still closed, in the real world turn your body to the left, slowly and fully but always comfortably, and then back to the center. Open your eyes. Lift your left arm and look at this imaginary watch, as you turn to the left as far as is comfortable. Then raise your eyes straight up and note where your line of vision falls on the wall now. Compare this point to the first measurement. Measure this difference with your hands.

See, you can do it all in your head.

Moshe's Exercise To Stretch the Sides

Lie down on your back. Scan your body. How does your head contact the carpet? What shape and size is the imprint your head makes on the carpet? How far is the back of your neck from the carpet? When does your spine touch the carpet again?

With your eyes closed, get a feeling for your right shoulder. Compare it with your left shoulder. Which shoulder is closer to the ceiling? Now see which shoulder is closer to which ear? Which shoulder makes the larger imprint on the carpet? Does this shoulder bear more weight? Go down your spine one inch at a time and see where the spine touches the floor and where it does not.

Compare the two sides of the pelvis. Which is closer to the ceiling? Which hip is closer to which shoulder? Which hip carries more weight into the floor? Which buttock makes the bigger imprint into the carpet? Do the backs of your knees touch the carpet? Look at how the right lower leg contacts the carpet. Does the leg lose contact with the carpet down near the heel? How far is this area off the carpet? Could a mouse run through without touching your leg? In what direction are your feet pointing? Does each foot point in the same direction? Do your toes point the same way as your feet? Are they curled up, or are some of them curled while some are straight?

Keep your body motionless except for your right arm. Move this arm so your hand slides gently under the small of your back. See how high off the floor the small of your back is and remember how curved or how flat these lumbar vertebrae are.

Place your right arm to your side with your palm down. Feel the carpet with your fingers. Slowly and gently, always slowly and gently, push your hand down a tiny bit toward your foot and then draw it slowly back to home base, the position where it originally was. Repeat this a few times. Be aware that your shoulder may want to move also. Let it move freely. Now increase the distance your hand moves down a little. What would make the movement easier? Try turning your head and looking at the hand as it goes toward the foot. Bring your head back to center when your arm returns to home base. Do this a few times. Stop that. This time turn your head and look at your hand when it is returning to home base. You look at your hand when it comes home and look away from the hand when the hand goes toward the foot. Try it a few times. Does this feel natural? Do it the other way. Does this feel more natural? More right?

See if your spine wants to get into the movement. Does it want to bend a little when the hand goes down and straighten when the hand comes back to home base? Let it move as it wants to. Does the action of the spine improve the movement of your hand? Is the movement more graceful, easier? Look again at just how your spine is moving. Does the upper part of the spine move to the right as the arm goes down and return straight when the arm comes back home? What happens to your pelvis? Does the pelvis move to the left when the arm goes down and the upper spine moves to the right? Does the lower spine move with the pelvis to the left as the upper spine moves to the right? Does this whole action assist the hand to make the small movement? Move your pelvis to the right as you move your upper spine to the right and push your hand down toward your feet. Take your time, move slowly, see what you are doing. Remember Moshe always said, "You cannot do what you want to do unless you know what you are doing." See if you can discern what you are doing. Can you do what you want to do? Do it gently, slowly, kindly, and lovingly. Now stop all that and rest. Take a moment. Pull your knees up. Move or rest as you like for a few moments.

Now lie on your back, legs extended, arms to your sides, palms down. Move your right hand gently down toward your right foot and back. Make the movement graceful and pleasant. What happens to your head? What is your upper spine doing? Your lower spine? Your pelvis? Can you feel that the movement is getting

124

lighter and easier to do? Can you feel that the big muscles of the pelvis are making this possible? All of the big muscles of the body are attached to the pelvis. These big muscles can do the work of the body more easily and efficiently than the smaller muscles in the extremities of the body. The movement gets lighter and more graceful when the body uses what it has to its best advantage. Just remember what the movement was like the first time you did it today.

Now stop all that and bend your left knee. Stretch your right leg and push your right heel away from you toward the far wall. Let your leg move a little toward that wall then back to home base. Push your heel down away from you and then let it return back to home base. Do this many times.

What is happening to your pelvis? Does the right hip bone want to go down and the left one up? Then do they both return to home base? Allow this movement to take place. Does it make the movement of the heel easier? What is happening to the left foot as it stands on the floor? What does it want to do when the right heel goes down? When does the left heel want to pull and when does it want to push? Try pulling the left heel up when you push the right heel down and then reverse both movements. Does having the left heel do the opposite of what the right heel is doing seem right? Now stop that and have the right and left heels both go down at the same time and both come back at the same time. Does this feel right? Try the reverse, moving them in opposite directions. Does one side of the pelvis come up when the other goes down? Does this feel right and appropriate? Is the movement more fluid and graceful? Are the big muscles of the pelvis giving the movement most of its power?

Stop that, and move the right hand and right heel down and up at the same time. Does it feel right to have them go in the same direction? Now move them in opposite directions. When the heel comes up, the hand goes down toward the heel. Then they both reverse and go away form each other. Do this a few times. Take the heel and the hand in the same direction. Is this the natural way? Does this feel correct? Do the tip of the spine and the bottom of the spine go in opposite directions? What happens to the head? Let it do what it wants. Let it get into the movement. Is the left foot assisting in the movement?

Stop that and take your right arm up above your head in the following way: keeping it palm down, slide your hand across the belly button, up over the chest and chin, across the top of the head. As your hand reaches your head, turn the palm toward the ceiling: then extend your arm over your head. Let the back of your hand rest on the carpet.

Bend your elbow until your whole arm, including the elbow, makes contact with the floor. Extend your arm slightly, just till your elbow leaves the floor. Then bring the arm aback. Bend the arm just enough to keep the elbow on the floor again. Repeat this movement many times. Now see if your arm is able to extend farther without lifting the elbow than it did when you first started the movement.

Move the right heel down and back a few times. Now move the arm and heel together. When the arm comes back to home, the heel is pushed down. When the arm extends, the heel moves back to home base. They both go in the same direction. Do this many times. Now move them toward each other, then away form each other. Which is the natural way? Do it the natural, easy way. Stop that and rest.

Extend your right leg and lift your right heel just high enough to get a sheet of paper out from under it. Then let the leg relax and fall to the floor. Do this many times.

Stop that and lift both the arm and the leg together. See how much each weighs as you lift together. Now lift just the leg and see its weight. Lift the arm and experience its weight. Now lift both together and see if they got lighter. Do the movement a few times. Let it get easy and graceful.

Stop that and bring your arm back to your side. Bring it over the top of your head, rotating your hand so your palm is down. Then slide your palm over your belly and down to the floor at the side of your body. Relax and rest, legs extended. While resting, look at the two sides of your body. Which leg feels longer? Which side is longer? Which side lies flatter on the floor?

Now roll over and stand up. Close your eyes and see which side is freer and more relaxed? Look at one side of your face and compare it to the other. Note the outside edge of your right eye and compare it with the outside edge of the left eye. Compare the two outside corners of the mouth. Are they different? How? If you have a partner, face each other and look for differences in the two sides. Is one eye larger and more open than the other? Is one side of the face freer of wrinkles and tension than the other? Share your observations with your partner.

Now your are going to do the left side of your body in your mind. Lie on your back, arms to your sides, left leg extended, and the right leg bent with the sole of the right foot flat on the floor. Now in the real world push your left hand down a tiny bit and let it come back home. Experience what you feel when this movement is made. Stop that and push your left heel down just a tiny bit and let it return home. Experience the sensations that this tiny movement evokes.

Now in your imagination only, do not move—just imagine that you move. Do all the movements in your head and experience the same feelings that you had when you did the exercise on the right side. So in your imagination, move your left hand a tiny bit down toward your foot and back home. In your imagination, you can do this many times quite quickly. Be sure to recreate the same sensations that came up when the same movement was done on the right side. Stop that and rest.

Again in your mind's eye, move your hand down toward the foot and remember how the head wanted to move to look at the hand as it went down and to return to center when the hand returned to home. Remember how one end of the spine wanted to go in one direction, and the pelvis and other end wanted to go in the other direction. Remember this feeling. Let the movement happen in your imagination. As the left arm goes down, the upper spine wants to go to the left, and the pelvis and lower spine want to go to the right. Recreate this experience in your imagination on your left side. Feel how the large muscles of the pelvis are helping the movement.

Stop that, and in the real world take the left hand down toward the feet. Can you see that the movement is now more graceful, lighter, and more mobile than a few minutes before?

Again in your imagination only, extend your leg so the left heel moves toward the far wall, and then let it return home. Do this many times. The right knee is bent with the right foot standing on

127

the floor. In your imagination only, push and pull with the right foot to help the imagined movement of the left heel. Feel how the right foot can help the imagined movement of the left heel, just as the left foot did for the right heel when you were working the right leg in the real world. Remember how the pelvis moved up and down in assisting the heel to push down and return home. Recreate that feeling.

Stop that and take the left hand over the head in the real world in the same way you did on the right side. Let the arm lie flat on the carpet, elbow and all. Now in your imagination, extend your arm until the elbow lifts from the carpet, then let it return. In your imagination experience this movement just as you did on the right side. Feel what the head, spine and pelvis want to do and let this happen in your imagination.

Stop that, and in your imagination push your left heel down and then let it return to home base. Do this many times in your imagination.

Stop that and in your imagination extend and lift the left hand off the carpet and back, just a tiny little bit off the carpet and back. Do this many times. Experience how heavy the arm is.

Stop that, and in your imagination lift the left leg up and down, just a tiny bit up and back. Experience how heavy the leg is. Do this many times.

Stop that, and in your imagination lift the arm and leg together. Sense how much lighter the leg and arm are when they are both lifted together. Now still in your imagination lift just your leg by itself a few times. Stop that and lift your arm by itself. Experience how heavy it is. Lift the two together in your imagination and see if they are not lighter.

Stop that, come back to the real world, stretch out, and rest. Are the two sides of your body more symmetrical? Do they feel the same length? In the real world stretch both arms above your head, the backs of your hands lying flat on the carpet, and lift your right leg and left arm at the same time and back to home base at the same time. Is this easier than lifting the arm and leg on the same side? Try it. Lift the right arm and right leg at the same time. Now lift a diagonal pair and see which is easier. Lift the other diagonal pair. Which pair is lighter?

Basic Instructions in Zazen

Zazen is the basic practice of Zen Buddhism because it provides the easiest conditions in which to experience a heightened state of awareness. Zazen cultivates sensitivity to subtle bodily sensations and connections and to the flow of energy. It also clears and increases your own vital energy. Sayama writes:

> It is an imitation of the form of Shakamuni under the Bo tree. *Zazen* releases awareness from conscious control. . . . In psychodynamic terms it can be said to cultivate the vital energy needed to realize higher level structures from the Unconscious. All Zen masters have practiced *Zazen*. Yet it should be remembered that Nan-yueh mocked Ma-tsu's efforts at sitting *zazen* to become a Buddha by polishing a stone with his sleeve to make a mirror.
>
> Significant physiological changes occur in a person practicing *zazen*. These include changes in brain waves from beta to alpha to theta, a lowered respiratory rate but increased respiratory volume, lack of habituation and reduced reaction time to a clicking stimulus, increased physical stability, and decreased muscular tension. It is also thought that the focus and pressure on the lower abdomen favorably stimulate the autonomic nervous system and circulate blood stored in the liver and spleen, thus effectively acting like a second heart.[1]

The instructions which follow are excerpted from *An Introduction to Zen Discipline* by Omori Sogen Rotaishi, Dharma successor to the Tenryu-ji line of Rinzai Zen.

> To sit zazen well, one must harmonize the mind, body, and breathing. Only when the three are realized as one, will it be possible to succeed in stabilizing and tranquilizing the body and mind at the dame time. Any one of these three things is inseparably related to the other two.[2]

Precautions

Beginners tend to overstrain the area of the lower abdomen because of the emphasis put on this area. Each individual is different in his physical structure and so must guide himself accordingly. One should sit in such a way as to cause his energy to pervade the whole body instead of forcing himself to put physical pressure on the lower abdomen. Only after long experience in the practice of zazen can one comprehend the difference between spiritual and physical power. The truth is only in the state of Mu; one is brought into the state of emptiness through diligent concentration of the power of the whole body at the tanden and simultaneously infusing the whole body with the vital energy radiating from there.

As zazen is not a test of quiet endurance, it is meaningless to sit for long periods without concentrating and unifying the mind and body. Thirty or forty minutes which is the time one incense stick takes to burn is adequate for beginners. Of course five or ten minutes will be enough if we sit fully and seriously. The crucial point is the degree of concentration rather than the length of sitting.

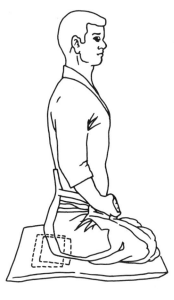

Figure A-1. Placement of Cushions
Select a wide cushion and two or three small ones. Stack the smaller ones under the wide one so they act as a wedge. Sit on the edge with the buttocks off the center of the wedge.

Figure A-2. The Full and Half Lotus Positions
To take the full lotus position as shown on the left, place the right foot near the base of the left thigh, and place the left foot on the right thigh.

To take the half lotus position as shown on the right, simply place the left foot on the right thigh or the right foot on the left thigh.

131

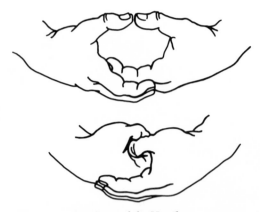

Figure A-3. Positions of the Hands

In the top position place the left hand with palm up and fingers together on the palm of the right hand. The inner sides of the tips of both thumbs touch, creating an ellipse. Viewed from above, the thumbs must be in line with the middle fingers.

In the alternate bottom position grasp the tip of the left thumb between the web of the thumb and the index finger of the right hand. Form a loose fist with the right hand and enclose it with the left.

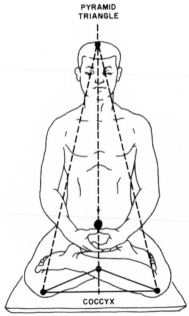

Figure A-4. Stabilizing the Body (front view, Full Lotus Position)

A well seated and very stable body is in the form of a pyramid. The base is an imaginary triangle formed by the lines connecting the two knees and the coccyx. The diagonal ridge lines extending from the two knees and the coccyx to the top of the head complete the pyramid.

Rock the body from right to left and again from left to right. The amplitude of this oscillation should be large at first and gradually decrease until the body stops moving and becomes stable.

132

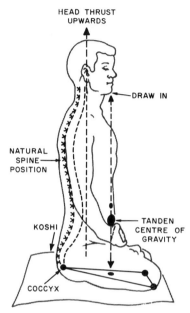

HEAD THRUST
UPWARDS

DRAW IN

NATURAL
SPINE
POSITION

KOSHI

TANDEN
CENTRE OF
GRAVITY

COCCYX

Figure A-5. Stabilizing the Body (side view)

a. Straighten the spine perpendicularly by inclining the upper body forward. Then, push the buttocks backward without moving it while raising the upper body gradually as if to push heaven with the back of the head. This action will straighten the spine into a natural position.

b. Advance the lower abdomen forward to straighten the hips. Raise the upper body until it becomes perpendicular with the neck upright and the lower jaw drawn in. The center of gravity will now coincide with the geometrical center of the plane triangle.

c. Check and see that the lower jaw is drawn in and the back of the neck is straight. If they are in the correct position, the ears and shoulders should fall in the same perpendicular plane.

d. Check also the position of the lower abdomen and the hips. If the lower abdomen is forward and the hip bone is upright, the nose and navel should be aligned.

e. Let the tip of the tongue touch the upper jaw with the teeth in light contact with each other.

f. Sit at ease, heavily and in alert dignity like Mt. Fuji soaring into heaven and overlooking the Eastern Seas.

133

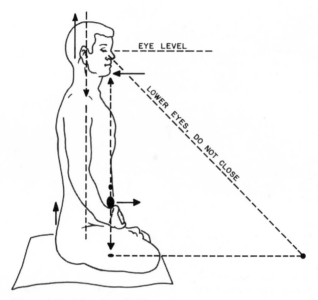

EYE LEVEL

LOWER EYES, DO NOT CLOSE

Figure A-6. Adjusting the Vision

Adjusting the vision helps to focus attention to prevent it from being taken up by internal or external stimuli.

a. The eyes should look straight ahead, and the visual field should span 180 degrees. Lower the eyes to a fixed position on the floor approximately three feet ahead. The eyes should be half-closed in selfless tranquility neither seeing nor not seeing anything.

b. Do not close the eyes. In order to enter the state of Zen concentration and to raise your inner power to the utmost, it is important to keep the eyes open. If one remains quiet with eyes closed like lifeless water, he will never be useful to society. It may seem easier to unify ourselves spiritually by closing the eyes, but then it will be inert zazen. Interpreting it more lightly, keeping the eyes open prevents us from falling asleep in meditation.

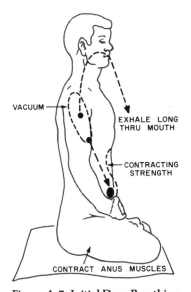
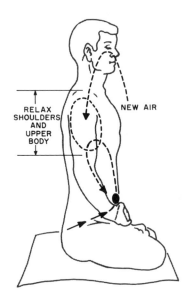

Figure A-7. Initial Deep Breathing

Deep breathing harmonizes the mind and the body.

a. Exhale slowly through the mouth as if to connect the atmosphere with the lower abdomen. Empty all the stale air with the strength created by the contraction of the lower abdomen. At the end of exhalation, relax the lower abdomen.

b. Due to atmospheric pressure, new air will naturally enter through the nose and fill the vacuum in the lungs.

c. After inhaling fully, pause slightly and with the koshi (Koshi and hara both refer to the lower abdomen, hips, lower back, and buttocks functioning as a unit. Koshi emphasizes the physical body, and hara has more spiritual significance.) extended forward, gently push the inhaled air into the lower abdomen in a scooping motion. The key to this is to contract the anus muscle.

d. Start exhaling again just before you feel uncomfortable. Repeat this type of breathing four to ten times.

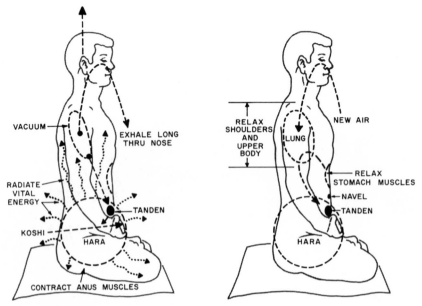

Figure A-8. Breathing in Meditation

a. When the respiration is adjusted, start breathing through the nose with the mouth closed. Inhaling is natural through the nose. Of course the inhaled air comes to the lungs but by relaxing the muscles around the pit of the stomach, you can actually feel the air filling the area below the navel.

b. Exhale through the nose. The breath should be long and directed toward the tanden with the power of the abdominal muscles. Contract the muscles around the anus and push the hips upright and slightly forward. The power should feel as if coming out of the area below the navel. In the process of exhaling powerfully, the pressure on the lower abdomen recesses the stomach area. The concentration on the lower extremities of the body should relax the shoulders and the upper body.

c. Inhaling should be left to occur naturally as new air fills the vacuum in the lungs.

d. Beginners should practice breathing with the tanden on purpose, but gradually conscious effort will lessen and the frequency of breathing will naturally decrease. In exhaling and inhaling, concentrate energy rather than physical power on the lower abdomen. When the vital power is at the tanden and confined in the hara, this spiritual strength and vital energy will radiate through the entire body.

e. Count your respiration with all of your spiritual power as if trying to penetrate to the core of the earth. Count the frequency of the exhalation from one to ten. Count in syllables as long as the exhalation. 0..........ne. T..........wo. And so on. Let your mind's eye follow the exhaled air in counting. If you miscount before reaching the count of ten or count beyond ten, start again from one.

f. In order to avoid incongruence between your respiration and the count, it is essential to concentrate your mind on the count rather than on the respiration as such, and feel as if you are breathing in accordance with the count.

NOTES

My Transformation

1. I wanted to leave this first chapter out but was voted down by those who had a hand in putting the book together.

Fascia

1. Ida Rolf, *Explorers of Humankind*, ed. Thomas Hanna (New York: Harper and Row, 1979), p.55.
2. Ibid., p. 56.
3. Ida Rolf, *Ida Rolf Talks about Rolfing and Physical Reality* (New York: Harper and Row, 1978), p. 70.

Movement and Awareness

1. Moshe Feldenkrais, "Awareness through Movement," *The 1975 Annual Handbook for Group Facilitators*, ed. John Jones and William Pfeiffer, (La Jolla, Ca.: University Associates Publishers, 1975).
2. Moshe Feldenkrais, Unpublished transcript of two lectures given at Copenhagen Congress of Functional Movement and Relaxation.
3. *Ibid.*
4. *Ibid.*
5. *Ibid.*
6. *Ibid.*
7. *Ibid.*

Dubbing

1. Janet Travell and David Simons, *Myofascial Pain and Dysfunction* (Baltimore: Williams and Wilkins, 1983), p. 4.

Vital Energy

1. Mike Sayama, *Samadhi, Self Development in Zen, Swordsmanship, and Psychotherapy* (New York: State University of New York Press, 1986), p. 78.

2. *Ibid.*, pp. 80–81.

3. *Ibid.*, p. 80.

4. Jackson Morisawa, *Zen Kyudo* (Honolulu: International Zen Dojo, 1985), p. 78.

5. Sayama, p. 86.

Reversing the Aging Process

1. James Fries and Lawrence Crapo, *Vitality and Aging* (San Francisco: W. H. Freeman, 1981), p. 109.

2. Thomas Hanna, "The Myth of Aging," *Somatics*, III, 4 (Spring/Summer, 1982), p. 17.

Appendix: Exercises To Reverse the Aging Process

1. Mike Sayama, *Samadhi* (New York: State University of New York Press, 1986), pp. 119–120.

2. Omori Sogen, Unpublished translation of *An Introduction to Zen Discipline.*

BIBLIOGRAPHY

Feldenkrais, Moshe. "Awareness through Movement," *The 1975 Annual Handbook for Group Facilitators*. ed. John Jones and William Pfeiffer. La Jolla: University Associates, 1975.

————. Unpublished transcripts of two lectures given at Copenhagen Congress of Functional Movement and Relaxation.

Fries, James, & Crapo, Lawrence. *Vitality and Aging*. San Francisco: W. H. Freeman and Company, 1981.

Hanna, Thomas. "The Myth of Aging," *Somatics*. III, 4, Spring/Summer, 1982.

Morisawa, Jackson. *Zen Kyudo*. Honolulu: International Zen Dojo, 1985.

Omori, Sogen. *An Introduction to Zen Discipline*. Unpublished translation.

Rolf, Ida. *Ida Rolf Talks about Rolfing and Physical Reality*. New York: Harper and Row, 1978.

————. *Explorers of Humankind*. ed. Thomas Hanna. New York: 1979.

Sayama, Mike. *Samadhi, Self Development in Zen, Swordsmanship, and Psychotherapy*. New York: State University of New York Press, 1986.

Travell, Janet and Simons, David. *Myofascial Pain and Dysfunction, The Trigger Point Manual*. Baltimore: Williams and Wilkins, 1983.